LATIN FOR THE NEW MILLENNIUM

STUDENT WORKBOOK

Second Edition LEVEL 2

LATIN FOR THE NEW MILLENNIUM

Series Information

LEVEL ONE

Student Text, Second Edition

Student Workbook, Second Edition

College Exercise Book, Levels 1 and 2

Teacher's Manual, Second Edition

Teacher's Manual for Student Workbook, Second Edition

ENRICHMENT TEXTS

From Romulus to Romulus Augustulus:
Roman History for the New Millennium

The Original Dysfunctional Family:
Basic Classical Mythology for the New Millennium

LEVEL TWO

Student Text, Second Edition

Student Workbook, Second Edition

Teacher's Manual, Second Edition

Teacher's Manual for Student Workbook, Second Edition

ENRICHMENT TEXTS

From Rome to Reformation:
Early European History for the New Millennium

The Clay-footed SuperHeroes:
Mythology Tales for the New Millennium

LEVEL THREE

Student Text

Teacher's Manual

ENRICHMENT TEXTS

Latin 3: Select Latin Enrichment Readings

ELECTRONIC RESOURCES

www.lnm.bolchazy.com

www.bolchazy.com/ebooks.aspx

Quia Question Bank

STUDENT WORKBOOK

LEVEL 2

Second Edition

Milena Minkova and Terence Tunberg

Bolchazy-Carducci Publishers, Inc.
Mundelein, Illinois USA

Series Editor: LeaAnn A. Osburn

Second Edition
Volume Editor: Donald E. Sprague
Contributing Editors: Laurel Draper, Karen Lee Singh

First Edition
Volume Editors: LeaAnn A. Osburn, Donald E. Sprague
Contributing Editors: Laurie Haight Keenan, Vicki A. Wine
Cover Design & Typography: Adam Phillip Velez
Cover Illustration: Colosseum © Bettman/Corbis

Latin for the New Millennium
Student Workbook, Level 2
Second Edition

Milena Minkova and Terence Tunberg

First edition published 2009

Bolchazy-Carducci Publishers, Inc.
1570 Baskin Road
Mundelein, Illinois 60060
www.bolchazy.com

Printed in the United States of America
2018
by Kingery Printing Company

ISBN 978-0-86516-812-1

CONTENTS

PREFACE

This workbook contains exercises to be used with every chapter of *Latin for the New Millennium*, Level 2. If you finish a chapter and then do all of the exercises in the workbook linked to that chapter, your grasp of the material in each chapter will be stronger. There are various types of exercises included in this workbook.

- Some exercises require only that that a noun(s) be declined or that a verb(s) be conjugated. You should try to do these exercises from memory in order to check your mastery of forms.
- The second exercise in each chapter of the workbook, like the second exercise in each chapter of the textbook, is devoted to English words derived from their Latin ancestors.
- Other exercises in various formats (e.g., fill-in-the-blank, change given forms to another specified form, etc.) are designed to give you practice with manipulating the forms of Latin and thereby gain a greater facility with the language.
- There are different types of translation exercises in this workbook: Latin to English translation, English to Latin translation, and translations of phrases. These exercises allow you to determine how well you understand the syntax and forms of the Latin language.
- Exercises based on new passages of Latin literature, while providing you with additional practice in the way Roman authors wrote, also give you the opportunity to read the writings of some authors not included in the textbook.
- Comprehension exercises let you see the progress you are making at understanding written Latin.
- At the end of each chapter in the workbook, you will find a series of Content Questions related to each chapter. Be sure to answer all the Content Questions as a way to check your mastery of the material.

At the back of this workbook, you will find the same English to Latin glossary and Latin to English glossary that is in your textbook. These are included in the workbook for your convenience as you do the exercises.

MM & TT
2017

CHAPTER 1

▶ EXERCISE 1

Conjugate in the present active and passive subjunctive.

vocō, vocāre, vocāvī, vocātum

Active

	Singular	Plural
First person	__________	__________
Second person	__________	__________
Third person	__________	__________

Passive

	Singular	Plural
First person	__________	__________
Second person	__________	__________
Third person	__________	__________

▶ EXERCISE 2

Match the word in Column A to the meaning of the Latin word in Column B from which it is derived. Meanings may be used more than once or not at all.

Column A		Column B	
1. ____	insolation	A.	seize
2. ____	*Le Monde*	B.	promise
3. ____	pisciculture	C.	find
4. ____	morose	D.	today
5. ____	isolation	E.	island
6. ____	inventory	F.	world
7. ____	indigenous	G.	fish
8. ____	occupy	H.	advice
9. ____	parasol	I.	produce
10. ____	progeny	J.	habit
		K.	sun
		L.	inhabitant

▶ EXERCISE 3

Change the present indicative forms into the present subjunctive, keeping the same person and number.

Example: sumus sīmus

1. possunt ______________________
2. potes ______________________
3. estis ______________________
4. sunt ______________________
5. possum ______________________
6. es ______________________
7. potest ______________________
8. possumus ______________________
9. sum ______________________
10. est ______________________
11. sunt ______________________

▶ EXERCISE 4

Translate the following imperative forms, give the corresponding subjunctive forms, and translate the changed forms.

Example: occupā!
occupy! occupēs you should/may occupy!

1. stāte!

   ________________ ________________ ________________

2. servā!

   ________________ ________________ ________________

3. sēparāte!

   ________________ ________________ ________________

4. rogā!

   ________________ ________________ ________________

5. iūdicā!

   ________________ ________________ ________________

▶ EXERCISE 5

Change the following sentences from the indicative into the subjunctive mood and translate them. Then change the positive subjunctives into the negative.

Example: Cōnsilia mihi datis.
Cōnsilia mihi dētis! You should/may give me advice!
Nōlīte mihi cōnsilia dare!

1. Ad ortum sōlis nāvigātis.

   ______________________ ______________________________

   ____

2. In partibus septentriōnālibus habitātis.

   ______________________ ______________________________

   ____

3. Ad merīdiem ambulās.

   ______________________ ______________________________

   ____

4. Bonōs mōrēs servātis.

   ______________________ ______________________________

   ____

5. Fortis mīles es.

   ______________________ ______________________________

   ____

▶ EXERCISE 6

Change the following sentences so that they express a wish. Translate the wish. Then change them into the negative if they are positive or into the positive if they are negative.

Example: Haec gēns nōn est plēna hostium.
Utinam nē haec gēns sit plēna hostium. May this population not be full of enemies!
Utinam haec gēns sit plēna hostium!

1. Potestis invenīre novam patriam.

 ______________________ ______________________

 ____

2. Hoc tibi prōmittere possum.

 ______________________ ______________________

 ____

3. Haec gēns nōn est crūdēlis.

 ______________________ ______________________

 ____

4. Sumus amīcī.

 ______________________ ______________________

 ____

5. Hominēs externī ab hāc gente nōn putāmur.

 ______________________ ______________________

 ____

The shamrock, also known as a trefoil, is readily recognized as symbolic of Patrick. When trying to explain the Christian concept of the trinity to the native Celts, legend tells us, Patrick used the native shamrock with its three leaves as comparable to the three-in-one God: God the Father, the Son, and the Holy Spirit.

▶ EXERCISE 7

Even before Bede, in the fifth century the famous Patrick—who is still today the patron saint of Ireland—a Romano-Briton, brought Christianity, and with it the use of Latin, to Ireland, an area that had never been a part of the Roman Empire. He is believed to have died on March 17th (St. Patrick's Day). Translate the passage about Patrick into English.

Patricius, quī erat incola Britanniae, ā latrōnibus ex Britanniā in Hiberniam est abductus. Patricius omnia facere dēbēbat quae latrōnēs iubēbant. Quōdam diē ille in somnō angelum vīdit. "Ad aliās terrās ambulēs," dīxit angelus, "et hominibus dē Deō nārrēs." Patricius ā latrōnibus fūgit, multās terrās petīvit et multās rēs audīvit. Tum in Hiberniam vēnit et Hibernīs ea quae sciēbat nārrāvit. Hibernī etiam nunc colunt et putant eum esse Hiberniae patrōnum.

____

____

____

____

____

____

____

____

abdūcō, ere, abdūxī, abductum – to kidnap, abduct
angelus, ī, *m.* – angel
Britannia, ae, *f.* – Britain
Hibernia, ae, *f.* – Ireland
Hibernus, ī, *m.* – Irishman
latrō, latrōnis, *m.* – bandit
Patricius, ī, *m.* – Patrick
patrōnus, ī, *m.* – patron, protector
quōdam diē – one day

This imposing granite statue of Patrick stands on Slieve Patrick just outside of Downpatrick in County Down, Ireland. Set up in 1932, the statue commemorates the 1,500th anniversary of Patrick's arrival in Ireland.

CONTENT QUESTIONS

After completing Chapter 1, answer these questions.

1. When and where did Bede live? What was his most important work?

   ____

   ____

2. What is the starting point of Bede's work?

   ____

3. What is the difference in meaning between the indicative and the subjunctive?

   ____

4. What is an optative expression?

   ____

5. What is the characteristic vowel of the present subjunctive of the first conjugation verbs?

   ____

6. What vowel appears in the present subjunctive of the verbs *sum* and *possum*?

   ____

Bede holding an open book from a woodcut in the *Liber Chronicārum Mundī* (*Book of the Chronicles of the World*) also known as the *Nuremberg Chronicle*. Compiled by Hartmann Schedel (1440–1514), a Nuremberg physician and humanist, the chronicle is considered one of the finest examples of early printed books.

CHAPTER 2

▶ EXERCISE 1

Conjugate in the present active and passive subjunctive.

1. *doceō, docēre, docuī, doctum*

Present Active Subjunctive: *doceō*

	Singular	Plural
First person	______________	______________
Second person	______________	______________
Third person	______________	______________

Present Passive Subjunctive: *doceō*

	Singular	Plural
First person	______________	______________
Second person	______________	______________
Third person	______________	______________

2. *sinō, sinere, sīvī, situm*

Present Active Subjunctive: *sinō*

	Singular	Plural
First person	______________	______________
Second person	______________	______________
Third person	______________	______________

Present Passive Subjunctive: *sinō*

	Singular	Plural
First person	______________	______________
Second person	______________	______________
Third person	______________	______________

3. *sentiō, sentīre, sēnsī, sēnsum*

Present Active Subjunctive: *sentiō*

	Singular	Plural
First person	______________	______________
Second person	______________	______________
Third person	______________	______________

Present Passive Subjunctive: *sentiō*

	Singular	Plural
First person	______________	______________
Second person	______________	______________
Third person	______________	______________

4. *accipiō, accipere, accēpī, acceptum*

Present Active Subjunctive: *accipiō*

	Singular	Plural
First person	______________	______________
Second person	______________	______________
Third person	______________	______________

Present Passive Subjunctive: *accipiō*

	Singular	Plural
First person	______________	______________
Second person	______________	______________
Third person	______________	______________

▶ EXERCISE 2

Which of the following is **NOT** derived from the same Latin word?

	a.	b.	c.	d.
1. _____	a. argent	b. Argentina	c. argentiferous	d. argue
2. _____	a. annul	b. annalist	c. annuity	d. superannuate
3. _____	a. oriole	b. orifice	c. auriferous	d. aureole
4. _____	a. equestrienne	b. equine	c. equal	d. equestrian
5. _____	a. grief	b. gravitate	c. grave	d. gregarious
6. _____	a. brier	b. abridge	c. brief	d. abbreviate
7. _____	a. declaration	b. clarinet	c. cleric	d. chanticleer
8. _____	a. belligerent	b. geriatric	c. suggest	d. indigestion
9. _____	a. interval	b. equivalent	c. prevail	d. valuable
10. _____	a. oboe	b. haughty	c. contralto	d. alter
11. _____	a. financial	b. paraffin	c. defiant	d. affinity
12. _____	a. investigate	b. vestment	c. invest	d. travesty
13. _____	a. disavow	b. vouch	c. provoke	d. volcano
14. _____	a. matinal	b. matter	c. matins	d. matinee

▶ EXERCISE 3

Translate into Latin.

1. Wear nice attire! ______________________________
2. Let us always be in good health! ______________________________
3. Do not allow this! ______________________________
4. Let us hate gold! ______________________________
5. May I have gold and silver! ______________________________
6. May there be no quarrels! ______________________________

▶ EXERCISE 4

Fill in the blanks with the correct form of the noun in parentheses and translate the completed sentence.

Example: Atticus ___Rōmae___ vīvēbat. (Rōma)
Atticus lived in Rome.

1. __________ sunt multae pulchrae urbēs. Eāmus (*let us go*) __________. Nē __________ discedāmus. (Italia)

   ____

2. Imperātōrēs Rōmānī __________ vīvēbant. Omnēs __________ venīre cupiēbant. Hominēs nōn cupiēbant __________ discēdere. (Rōma)

   ____

3. Carolus Magnus domum suam __________ habuit. Carolus __________ nōn discēdēbat. (Aquīsgrānum)

   ____

4. __________ multī equitēs inveniuntur. (Gallia)

   ____

5. Multa __________ docēbantur. Eī, quī docērī cupiunt, __________ veniant! (Athēnae)

   ____

6. Magnum odium contrā Rōmānōs __________ crēscēbat. Odium __________ nōn discēdēbat. (Carthāgō)

   ____

The art nouveau style clock overlooks the Hoher Markt in Vienna, Austria, where every hour a famous person appears, including Marcus Aurelius and Charlemagne. The Roman commander's palace at the Vindobona camp, where Emperor Marcus Aurelius died, was located at what is today the Hoher Markt. Vienna served as the capital for the Hapsburg Holy Roman Emperors.

The following three exercises are adapted from Suetonius (75–150 CE) whose collection of biographies *On the Lives of the Emperors* was used by Einhard as an example for his biography of Charlemagne. You read some Latin passages adapted from Suetonius in the workbook, Chapter 17, of Level 1.

This bust of Charlemagne casts him as a Roman emperor—hair and beard style, laurel crown, and dress. Through the centuries, rulers have regularly identified themselves with their Roman emperor predecessors or artists have cast them in that role.

TIMELINE

44 BCE	assassination of Julius Caesar
27 BCE–14 CE	Augustus
14 CE–37 CE	Tiberius
37 CE–41 CE	Caligula
41 CE–54 CE	Claudius
54 CE–68 CE	Nero
68 CE–69 CE	Galba
69 CE	Otho
69 CE	Vitellius
69 CE–79 CE	Vespasian

▶ EXERCISE 5

Translate into English.

Multī hominēs Claudium malē tractābant, cum nōn erat imperātor. Sī sērō ad cēnās veniēbat, aliī omnia comēderant nec cibōs eī relīquerant. Sī interdum cibus erat relictus, Claudiusque comēderat et obdormīverat, oleārum ossa in eum iacere solēbant. "Nōlīte rēs in mē iacere! Mē relinquātis in pāce!" dīcēbat Claudius. "In pāce relinquēris, sī ā cēnā discesseris," respondēbant irrīsōrēs. Sī Claudius dormiēbat, solēbant quoque soccōs in manūs eius pōnere. Tum ā somnō expergēfactus vultum soccīs cōnfricābat.

cēna, ae, *f.* – dinner
cibus, ī, *m.* – food
Claudius, ī, *m.* – Claudius
cōnfricō, āre, cōnfricuī, — – to rub
expergēfactus, a, um – awakened
irrīsor, irrīsōris, *m.* – mocker, derider
malē tractō, āre, āvī, ātum – to treat badly
obdormiō, īre, īvī, ītum – to fall asleep
olea, ae, *f.* – olive
os, ossis, *n.* – bone, seed, stone
sērō (*adv.*) – late
soccus, ī, *m.* – slipper

▶ EXERCISE 6

Translate into English.

Vitellius cibōs valdē amābat et magnās cēnās semper habēbat, in quibus multa fercula parābantur. Semel eī cēna data est ā frātre, in quā dum comedēbat, duo mīlia piscium, septem mīlia avium sunt apposita. Semper comedere cupiēbat. Sī Rōmae ambulābat et popīnam aspiciēbat, statim cibōs rapiēbat, etiam prīdiānōs vel sēmēsōs.

____

____

____

____

____

____

____

____

appōnō, ere, apposuī, appositum – to offer, serve
avis, avis, *f.* – bird
cēna, ae, *f.* – dinner
cibus, ī, *m.* – food
duo mīlia + *gen.* – two thousand
ferculum, ī, *n.* – dish
frāter, frātris, *m.* – brother
popīna, ae, *f.* – restaurant
prīdiānus, a, um – from the day before
rapiō, ere, rapuī, raptum – to snatch
semel (*adv.*) – once
sēmēsus, a, um – half-eaten
septem mīlia + *gen.* – seven thousand
Vitellius, ī, *m.* – Vitellius

▶ EXERCISE 7

Translate into Latin.

Caesar was captured by pirates. He was behaving as an emperor, not as a captured man. At last the ship came to the shore, money was given for Caesar, and he was freed. Afterward the pirates were captured and led to Caesar. They were asking him: "Take back your money and save us!" Caesar, however, sent them to death.

____

____

____

____

____

____

Caesar, Caesaris, *m.* – Caesar
pecūnia, ae, *f.* – money
pīrāta, ae, *m.* – pirate

CONTENT QUESTIONS

After completing Chapter 2, answer these questions.

1. What was the Holy Roman Empire?

2. Who was the first ruler of what became the Holy Roman Empire and when was he crowned?

3. Who was the author of Charlemagne's biography?

4. What author was a model for Charlemagne's biography?

5. What is the characteristic vowel of the present subjunctive for the second, third, fourth conjugation, and the third conjugation *–iō* verbs?

6. What is the locative?

This portrait, similar in style to that on the title page for Chapter 2 in the text, shows Charlemagne splendidly attired but as an old man.

CHAPTER 3

▶ EXERCISE 1

Conjugate in the imperfect active and passive subjunctive.

1. *sēparō, sēparāre, sēparāvī, sēparātum*

Imperfect Active Subjunctive: *sēparō*

	Singular	Plural
First person	__________	__________
Second person	__________	__________
Third person	__________	__________

Imperfect Passive Subjunctive: *sēparō*

	Singular	Plural
First person	__________	__________
Second person	__________	__________
Third person	__________	__________

2. *dēleō, dēlēre, dēlēvī, dēlētum*

Imperfect Active Subjunctive: *dēleō*

	Singular	Plural
First person	__________	__________
Second person	__________	__________
Third person	__________	__________

Imperfect Passive Subjunctive: *dēleō*

	Singular	Plural
First person	__________	__________
Second person	__________	__________
Third person	__________	__________

3. *scrībō, scrībere, scrīpsī, scrīptum*

Imperfect Active Subjunctive: ***scrībō***

	Singular	Plural
First person	________	________
Second person	________	________
Third person	________	________

Imperfect Passive Subjunctive: ***scrībō***

	Singular	Plural
First person	________	________
Second person	________	________
Third person	________	________

4. *sciō, scīre, scīvī, scītum*

Imperfect Active Subjunctive: ***sciō***

	Singular	Plural
First person	________	________
Second person	________	________
Third person	________	________

Imperfect Passive Subjunctive: ***sciō***

	Singular	Plural
First person	________	________
Second person	________	________
Third person	________	________

5. *accipiō, accipere, accēpī, acceptum*

Imperfect Active Subjunctive: ***accipiō***

	Singular	Plural
First person	________	________
Second person	________	________
Third person	________	________

Imperfect Passive Subjunctive: ***accipiō***

	Singular	Plural
First person	________	________
Second person	________	________
Third person	________	________

▶ EXERCISE 2

Choose the English derivative that comes from the Latin word provided.

		a.	b.	c.	d.
1. *iungō*	_____	a. adjust	b. joint	c. judge	d. adjective
2. *discō*	_____	a. disciplinary	b. dismal	c. disdain	d. dissipate
3. *frāter*	_____	a. fraud	b. refrain	c. friar	d. refract
4. *fāma*	_____	a. famine	b. family	c. famulus	d. fame
5. *dominus*	_____	a. domain	b. donation	c. subdue	d. sovereign
6. *salūs*	_____	a. salvage	b. salubrious	c. salmon	d. salad
7. *improbus*	_____	a. opprobrious	b. impropriety	c. probable	d. impudence
8. *pariō*	_____	a. apparent	b. separatist	c. partisan	d. grandparent
9. *perdō*	_____	a. perdition	b. pardon	c. parade	d. perdurable
10. *scrībō*	_____	a. scruple	b. scripture	c. scab	d. crib

▶ EXERCISE 3

Fill in the blanks with the correct form of the verbs in parentheses. Translate the sentences.

Example: Librum lēgī ut rēs ___discerem___. (discō)
I read the book in order to learn things.

1. Ambulāvī ut amīcōs _______________. (petō)

____

2. Vocāvit puerōs ut eōs _______________. (doceō)

____

3. Domī maneō ut librum scrībere _______________. (possum)

____

4. Mē occultāvī nē _______________. (inveniō)

____

5. Gladium habeō ut _______________ armātus. (esse)

____

6. Vēnī ut auxilium tibi _______________. (dō)

____

▶ EXERCISE 4

Translate into Latin.

1. I wrote you a letter so that you might read about me.

 ____

2. Read the letter so that you may learn about my affairs!

 ____

3. The girl sought him in order to learn about literature.

 ____

4. They hid everything so that bad things would not be heard.

 ____

5. We ought to be together in order to be happy.

 ____

6. We had to be together in order to be happy.

 ____

Republican Rome's most famous orator, philosopher, and writer Cicero is honored with a statue prominently placed on the Italian Palace of Justice in Rome. This palace serves as the headquarters for the Italian national government equivalent of the United States Department of Justice.

▶ EXERCISE 5

The following text is an adaptation of Cicero's letter to his wife Terentia in *Epistulae ad familiārēs* (*Letters to Relatives*, 16.1). At the time, Cicero was exiled in Greece and Terentia was in Rome. Translate the passage into English.

Cicero Terentiae suae salūtem dīcit.

Ex epistulīs multōrum hominum didicī tē hīs in rēbus difficilibus et hīs in perīculīs magnā animī fortitūdine agere. Scrīpsērunt enim ad mē ut dē tē nārrārent. Nunc miser factus sum. Fortasse ego errāvī et nōs ad fūnesta dūxī. Intellegō tē propter mē valdē dolēre. Lacrimae iam nōn sinunt mē scrībere. Nōn scrībam nē tū quoque lacrimīs opprimāris. At tū ad mē scrībās ut dē tē et dē fīliīs sciam. Valē, Terentia mea, vīta mea!

____

____

____

____

____

____

____

____

____

____

▶ EXERCISE 6

Translate the following passage. It is loosely based on a poetic letter (*Poem* 5) by Sulpicia, a poet who lived toward the end of the first century BCE. The recipient of her poetry was a certain Cerinthus (ī, m.), probably a fictitious person.

You ought to know, Cerinthus, that I am not in good health. I wrote to you so that you may know that. Are you thinking about your girl? But if I fight (*use future perfect*) in order to overcome the illness, my heart (chest) will suffer anyway the illness of love.

____

____

____

____

labōrō, āre, āvī, ātum + *abl.* – to suffer from

morbus, ī, *m.* – illness

▶ EXERCISE 7

In Chapter 16 of Level 1, you read Pliny the Younger's account of the eruption of Vesuvius. Here you will read an adapted version incorporating two of Pliny's letters to Calpurnia (*Epistulae* 6.4; 7.5). Calpurnia was Pliny the Younger's third and very young wife. Pliny's letters to Calpurnia are famous for the tenderness of the sentiment expressed in them.

Translate the text into English.

Plīnius Calpurniae suae salūtem dīcit.

Scrībō ad tē, mea uxor, ut verba mea tibi dīcant mē tē egēre. Sine tē dormīre nōn possum et noctū vultum tuum ante oculōs habeō. Interdum conclāve tuum petō ut sentiam mē tēcum ibi esse. Sciās mē saepe negōtiīs occupārī nē propter absentiam tuam nimium doleam. Animus dē omnibus sollicitātur, omnia timet. Mittās epistulam mox! Dum legam, nōn sollicitābor nec timēbō; postquam lēgerō, statim sollicitābor, statim timēbō. Haec scrīpsī ut dē marītō tuō legerēs. Bene valeās!

____

____

____

____

____

____

____

____

____

____

____

____

____

absentia, ae, *f.* – absence
conclāve, conclāvis, *n.* – room
negōtium, ī, *n.* – business, political activity
nimium (*adv.*) – too much
sollicitō, āre, āvī, ātum – to worry

In 1150 Hildegard moved with her group of nuns to Rupert Mountain, conveniently located by the Rhine and Nahe Rivers. She began construction of a new monastery over the grave of St. Rupert. Two years later, a three-nave church was built. Most of Hildegard's writings were executed as manuscripts in the scriptorium of the monastery. In 1632, during the Thirty Years War, the Swedes destroyed the monastery. Later the buildings were quarried for the construction of farm buildings leaving only the church untouched. The nineteenth century saw further destruction when the rock was blown up to accommodate the path of the railroad. Nonetheless, five arcade arches of the former monastery church are preserved in a complex of vaulted cellars. The Rupertsberger vault depicted here is maintained by the Rupertsberger Historical Society. Note the statue of Hildegard on the right.

▶ EXERCISE 8

In 2012, Pope Benedict XV proclaimed Hildegard von Bingen (1098–1179) both a saint and a doctor of the church. Joining thirty-four other "doctors of the church," Hildegard became only the fourth woman to be so honored. Born the tenth child to a noble family, as was customary with the tenth child, Hildegard was dedicated at birth to the church. At age eight, she was sent to live with the holy woman Jutta. Upon her teacher's death thirty years later, Hildegard was elected head of the growing religious community that under her leadership became a vibrant convent known for its musical productions. Known as the "Sybil of the Rhine," Hildegard wrote major works on theology, composed musical plays, and recorded her mystical experiences and visions, which had begun when she was a child. She was an expert on natural healing and wrote treatises on natural history and the curative powers of natural elements. Her wisdom was recognized throughout Europe and her advice was sought by kings, bishops, and popes.

Music was especially important to Hildegard. She contended that before the Fall, Adam enjoyed a pure voice and with the angels praised God in song. For Hildegard, who composed hymns in honor of saints, virgins, and the Virgin Mary, music helps humankind recapture the original joy and beauty of paradise.

Translate Hildegard's hymn into English.

Ō quam mīrābilis
est prescientia dīvīnī pectoris,
que prescīvit omnem creātūram.
Nam cum Deus inspēxit faciem hominis,
quem formāvit, (5)
omnia opera sua in eādem formā
hominis integra aspēxit.
O quam mīrābilis est inspīrātiō,
que hominem sic suscitāvit.

____

____

____

____

____

____

____

____

____

creātūra, ae, *f.* – creature
formō, āre, āvī, ātum – shape, form
inspiciō, ere, spexī, spectum – to look into, look at
inspīrātiō, ōnis, *f.* – breathing into, inspiration
integer, gra, grum – complete, whole
mīrābilis, mīrābile – marvelous, wondrous
opus, eris, *n.* – work, workmanship, achievement
prescientia, ae, *f.* – foreknowledge
presciō, īre, īvī, ītum – to know before
que = quae
suscitō, āre, āvī, ātum – to encourage, stir up

CONTENT QUESTIONS

After completing Chapter 3, answer these questions.

1. When did Abelard live?

    ____

2. From what work do we learn details about Abelard's tragic love story?

    ____

3. For what reason did Abelard remain famous in addition to his love for Heloise?

    ____

    ____

4. How would you easily recognize the imperfect subjunctive?

    ____

5. Which tenses are called primary and which secondary?

    ____

6. What is the sequence of tenses?

    ____

    ____

7. What was the name of Abelard's and Heloise's son?

    ____

This engraving shows two scientists using the astrolabe. In the foreground, the scientist is using the astrolabe to measure the distance from the top of the well to the water below. His colleague demonstrates how the astrolabe uses angles to measure altitude. Note the lines from the astrolabe to the castle.

CHAPTER 4

▶ EXERCISE 1

Conjugate the following verbs in the perfect active subjunctive.

1. *parcō, parcere, pepercī, —*

Perfect Active Subjunctive: ***parcō***

	Singular	**Plural**
First person	______________	______________
Second person	______________	______________
Third person	______________	______________

2. *furō, furere, furuī, —*

Perfect Active Subjunctive: ***furō***

	Singular	**Plural**
First person	______________	______________
Second person	______________	______________
Third person	______________	______________

▶ EXERCISE 2

Select the meaning of the Latin word from which the given English word is derived.

1. agminate	_____	a. line of march	b. rampart	c. move	d. lead
2. pontificate	_____	a. priest	b. bridge	c. weigh	d. pony
3. porch	_____	a. harbor	b. carry	c. part	d. gate
4. lignify	_____	a. light	b. unite	c. wood	d. dispute
5. quantitative	_____	a. how much	b. when	c. four	d. what sort
6. tutor	_____	a. you	b. teacher	c. whole	d. safe
7. vacation	_____	a. road	b. empty	c. cow	d. weary
8. overt	_____	a. turn	b. increase	c. open	d. begin
9. parsimonious	_____	a. obey	b. prepare	c. equal	d. spare
10. recipe	_____	a. receive	b. cook	c. part	d. cut
11. invasion	_____	a. wander	b. burst in	c. become stronger	d. weaken
12. furious	_____	a. thief	b. branch	c. rage	d. heat
13. convalescent	_____	a. be strong	b. become weak	c. agree	d. assemble

▶ EXERCISE 3

Conjugate the following verbs in the pluperfect active subjunctive.

1. *ēdō, ēdere, ēdidī, ēditum*

Pluperfect Active Subjunctive: *ēdō*

	Singular	**Plural**
First person	_______________	_______________
Second person	_______________	_______________
Third person	_______________	_______________

2. *resistō, resistere, restitī, restitum*

Pluperfect Active Subjunctive: *resistō*

	Singular	**Plural**
First person	_______________	_______________
Second person	_______________	_______________
Third person	_______________	_______________

▶ EXERCISE 4

Translate into Latin.

1. May your rewards be great!

____

2. If only we had understood those words!

____

3. If only we were not in this city!

____

4. If only I had not seen so great a disaster!

____

5. May you not see so great a disaster!

____

6. If only we had understood what the soldiers were doing!

____

A close-up of Godfrey of Bouillon in his full crusader regalia from the nineteenth-century equestrian statue in the Place Royale in Brussels, Belgium. The statue was erected in 1843 in front of the Royal Palace as part of a statewide program of recognizing important figures in Belgium's history.

▶ EXERCISE 5

Translate into English.

1. Nōn sciēbāmus quī mīlitēs cum Godefrīdō urbem intrāvissent.

2. Vidētisne quantum incendium hostēs prope mūrōs fēcerint?

3. Discāmus ventusne in vultūs hostium flet!

4. Nārrābis nōbīs quam facile mīlitēs pontem ligneum aedificāverint.

5. Paucī intellēxērunt quantum agmen nostrōrum ad urbem vēnisset.

6. Incolae nōn facile vidēbant quī essent amīcī et quī essent hostēs.

▶ EXERCISE 6

Change the following direct questions into indirect questions using the verb in parentheses. Use the correct tense in the indirect question. Translate the changed sentences.

Example: Quae praemia accipiunt amīcī nostrī? (didicerāmus)
Didicerāmus quae praemia amīcī nostrī acciperent.
We had learned what rewards our friends were accepting.

1. Cūr nōs incendium prope mūrōs facere iussistī? (dīcēs)

2. Cūr carnem nōn coquere solētis? (nōn intellegō)

3. Quā dē causā incolīs nōn pepercērunt? (utinam discās)

4. Quam celeriter portam aperuerant aliōsque mīlitēs admīserant? (didicimus)

____

____

5. Quī mīlitēs mūrum scandere possunt? (sciēbantne)

____

____

6. Cūr mīlitibus meīs nihil dedistī? (rogāvī)

____

____

▶ EXERCISE 7

Read the following questions. Choose the best answer for each question and translate both the question and the selected answer. The questions pertain to the Latin reading passage.

Example: Cūr Godefrīdus mīlitēs incendium magnum prope mūrōs facere iussit?

Hostēs mūrōs dēfendere dēbēbant.

Hostēs ē mūrīs fūgērunt.

Ventus in vultūs hostium flābat et fūmus in oculōs hostium agī poterat.

Why did Godfrey order <his> soldiers to build a large fire near the walls?
Ventus in vultūs hostium flābat et fūmus in oculōs hostium agī poterat.
The wind was blowing into the faces of the enemy and the smoke could be driven into the eyes of the enemy.

1. Quōmodo (*in what way*) mīlitēs quōs Godefrīdus dūcēbat mūrōs scandērunt?

   Mīlitēs Godefrīdī pontem ligneum aedificāvērunt.

   Mīlitēs Godefrīdī prope mūrōs erant.

   Mīlitēs Godefrīdī loca hostibus vacua iam occupāvērunt.

____

____

____

2. Cūr dux paucōs mīlitēs ad urbis portam septentriōnālem mīsit?

   Porta septentriōnālis dīcitur Sanctī Stephanī.

   Hoc fēcit, ut aliōs mīlitēs admitteret, quī extrā mūrōs exspectābant.

   Ingēns agmen Francōrum intrāvit.

____

____

____

3. Cūr incolae, quī cum Comitis Tolosānī mīlitibus pugnābant, subitō fugērunt?

   Incolae tandem intellēxērunt aliōs Francōs cum Godefrīdō urbem iam intrāvisse.

   Incolae prope montem Siōn pugnāre coepērunt.

   Incolae sē in arcem recēpērunt.

___

___

___

4. Cūr Francī tam crūdēliter (*cruelly*, adv.) omnēs incolās occīdērunt?

   Agmen mīlitum nostrōrum in partem urbis merīdiānam violenter invāsit.

   Francī īrā et dolōre incēnsī furēbant.

   Incolae territī sē in arcem recēpērunt et in templum fūgērunt.

___

___

___

An artist's rendition of a German crusader knight. Under the Holy Roman Emperor, the Germans contributed significantly to the Crusades. During the Third Crusade, they might have been successful in defeating Saladin's armies, had Emperor Frederick I Barbarossa not drowned on the way.

CONTENT QUESTIONS

After completing Chapter 4, answer these questions.

1. What were the two main reasons why the people of Western Europe responded to calls for crusades to the "Holy Land"?

   ____

2. Where was William of Tyre born?

   ____

3. What tenses of the subjunctive are used to express a wish for the future, a wish for the present, and a wish for the past?

   ____

4. What types of main verbs can have indirect questions depending on them?

   ____

5. Which tenses of the subjunctive can depend on primary tenses of the main verb and which on secondary tenses?

   ____

   ____

6. What form does the pluperfect active subjunctive seem to contain in itself?

   ____

CHAPTER 5

▶ EXERCISE 1

Conjugate the following verbs in the perfect and the pluperfect passive subjunctive.

1. *ōrō, ōrāre, ōrāvī, ōrātum*

Perfect Passive Subjunctive: *ōrō*

	Singular	Plural
First person	______________________	______________________
Second person	______________________	______________________
Third person	______________________	______________________

Pluperfect Passive Subjunctive: *ōrō*

	Singular	Plural
First person	______________________	______________________
Second person	______________________	______________________
Third person	______________________	______________________

2. *possideō, possidēre, possēdī, possessum*

Perfect Passive Subjunctive: *possideō*

	Singular	Plural
First person	______________________	______________________
Second person	______________________	______________________
Third person	______________________	______________________

Pluperfect Passive Subjunctive: *possideō*

	Singular	Plural
First person	______________________	______________________
Second person	______________________	______________________
Third person	______________________	______________________

3. *scrībō, scrībere, scrīpsī, scrīptum*

Perfect Passive Subjunctive: ***scrībō***

	Singular	Plural
First person	______________	______________
Second person	______________	______________
Third person	______________	______________

Pluperfect Passive Subjunctive: ***scrībō***

	Singular	Plural
First person	______________	______________
Second person	______________	______________
Third person	______________	______________

4. *inveniō, invenīre, invēnī, inventum*

Perfect Passive Subjunctive: ***inveniō***

	Singular	Plural
First person	______________	______________
Second person	______________	______________
Third person	______________	______________

Pluperfect Passive Subjunctive: ***inveniō***

	Singular	Plural
First person	______________	______________
Second person	______________	______________
Third person	______________	______________

5. *aspiciō, aspicere, aspexī, aspectum*

Perfect Passive Subjunctive: ***aspiciō***

	Singular	Plural
First person	______________	______________
Second person	______________	______________
Third person	______________	______________

Pluperfect Passive Subjunctive: ***aspiciō***

	Singular	Plural
First person	______________	______________
Second person	______________	______________
Third person	______________	______________

▶ EXERCISE 2

Choose the derivative that comes from the Latin word whose meaning is provided.

1. song	_____	a. canary	b. candid	c. card	d. Carmen
2. food	_____	a. ciborium	b. famish	c. edible	d. flesh
3. river	_____	a. irrigate	b. flume	c. stream	d. riparian
4. vice	_____	a. viticulture	b. inevitable	c. vicious	d. vicar
5. joke	_____	a. jointly	b. jostle	c. juicy	d. juggle
6. youth	_____	a. rejuvenate	b. adolescent	c. rejoice	d. adjutant
7. mind	_____	a. amend	b. demented	c. memory	d. mention
8. wine	_____	a. vindicate	b. vitiate	c. vinegar	d. vitreous
9. courage	_____	a. virulence	b. virus	c. virology	d. virtuoso
10. old	_____	a. veterinarian	b. devolve	c. vexatious	d. devoted
11. violent	_____	a. invective	b. vehement	c. reverberate	d. subversion
12. nearest	_____	a. prosperous	b. approbation	c. approximate	d. proprietor
13. drink	_____	a. revel	b. bicarbonate	c. ridicule	d. bib
14. ask	_____	a. adore	b. request	c. suborn	d. orifice
15. to please	_____	a. placate	b. pleasant	c. applaud	d. plaintive
16. light	_____	a. release	b. leniency	c. lever	d. relent

▶ EXERCISE 3

Fill in the blanks with the correct form of the verb in parentheses. Translate the sentences.

Example: Rogō quid ā tē ___sit factum___. (faciō).
I ask what has been done by you.

1. Quaerō (= *rogō*) quī cibī ā tē ____________. (cōnsūmō)

   ____

2. Scīre cupiō bonaene rēs ā nōbīs ____________. (petō)

   ____

3. Rogāvī ā quō homine malae rēs ____________. (faciō)

   ____

4. Nōn sciēbam ā quō vitia ____________. (amō)

   ____

5. Scīre cupiēbam quid ā tē ____________. (possideō)

   ____

To attract customers who were usually illiterate, medieval shops hung a readily recognized image outside their door. The miniature wooden barrel signified a wineshop. Medieval quarters in European cities often continue this tradition.

▶ EXERCISE 4

Translate into Latin. Use the verbs *ōrō,* "to entreat," *rogō,* "to ask," and *imperō, āre, āvī, ātum* + dative, "to order someone."

1. I ask you to cultivate good manners.

2. I ordered you to abandon bad manners.

3. They entreated us not to drink so much.

4. They ordered us to drink only water.

5. The mother and the father are asking the son to learn with constancy.

6. You (pl.) cannot order the poets to write nice poems.

▶ EXERCISE 5

Change each of the following sentences into indirect statements (after *putō*), indirect questions (after *rogō . . . ne*), and indirect commands (after *ōrō ut*). Translate each of the changed sentences.

Example: Librōs legis.

Putō tē librōs legere.	I think you are reading books.
Rogō librōsne legās.	I ask whether you are reading books.
Ōrō ut librōs legās.	I beg you to read books.

1. Iocī tē dēlectant.

2. Vīta saepe mūtātur.

3. Iuventūs est semper fēlīx.

▶ EXERCISE 6

Translate into Latin. Use the appropriate subjunctive (volitive, purpose clause, indirect command, indirect question) where necessary and *nōlī* + infinitive for a negative command. Identify the type of subjunctive construction.

Example: Think about poems; do not think about beautiful girls!
Cōgitēs dē carminibus; nōlī dē pulchrīs puellīs cōgitāre! (volitive subjunctive)

1. I wrote these poems so that you (pl.) might learn about my life.

   ____

2. You were asked to abandon the old life.

   ____

3. Let us drink and let us have joy! Let us not ever feel pain!

   ____

4. The poet begs the people who will read that he not be punished.

   ____

5. Do you understand why the life of the poet is similar to a ship without a sailor?

   ____

The wine goblet was an essential element of medieval tableware. This beautifully engraved goblet and tray would have graced a lord's table. University students would have made do with a roughly hewn wooden cup.

▶ EXERCISE 7

Read aloud the so-called *carmen pōtōrium*, "drinking song," excerpted in a very slightly adapted form from the *Carmina Burāna*. Observe its rhythm and rhyme. Translate it into English.

Bibit era, bibit erus,
bibit mīles, bibit clērus,
bibit ille, bibit illa,
bibit servus cum ancillā,
bibit cōnstāns, bibit vagus, (5)
bibit rudis, bibit magus.

Bibit pauper et aegrōtus,
bibit exsul et ignōtus,
bibit puer, bibit cānus,
bibit praesul et decānus, (10)
bibit soror, bibit frāter,
bibit anus, bibit māter,
bibit illa, bibit ille,
bibunt centum, bibunt mille.

____
____
____
____
____
____
____
____
____
____
____
____
____
____

aegrōtus, a, um – sick
ancilla, ae, *f.* – maidservant
anus, anūs, *f.* – old woman
cānus, a, um – gray-haired
centum – hundred
clērus, ī, *m.* – clergyman
cōnstāns, cōnstantis – constant, steady; remember *cōnstantia*
decānus, ī, *m.* – an ecclesiastical official who sometimes is a head of school: the word is "Dean" in English
era, ae, *f.* – mistress, lady of the manor
erus, ī, *m.* – lord
exsul, exsulis, *m.* – a person banished in exile
ignōtus, a, um – unknown
magus, ī, *m.* – a learned man or magician
mille – thousand
praesul, praesulis, *m.* – priest (or) bishop
rudis, rude – unformed, unskilled
servus, ī, *m.* – servant
vagus, a, um – wandering, unsteady

CONTENT QUESTIONS

After completing Chapter 5, answer these questions.

1. What is the *Carmina Burāna?*

2. Who was the author of *Cōnfessiō Goliae* and when did he live?

3. In what way is *Cōnfessiō Goliae* so different from ancient poetry?

4. What is the difference in forming the perfect and pluperfect indicative passive on the one hand, and the perfect and pluperfect subjunctive passive on the other?

5. With what conjunctions is an indirect command introduced?

6. What tenses of the subjunctive are used in an indirect command and in what circumstances?

CHAPTER 6

▶ EXERCISE 1

Decline the following phrases.

1. *rēx crūdēlior*

	Singular	Plural
Nominative	______________________	______________________
Genitive	______________________	______________________
Dative	______________________	______________________
Accusative	______________________	______________________
Ablative	______________________	______________________
Vocative	______________________	______________________

2. *praemium pulchrius*

	Singular	Plural
Nominative	______________________	______________________
Genitive	______________________	______________________
Dative	______________________	______________________
Accusative	______________________	______________________
Ablative	______________________	______________________
Vocative	______________________	______________________

▶ EXERCISE 2

Which of the following is **NOT** derived from the same Latin word?

	a.	b.	c.	d.
1. _____	a. heirloom	b. heinous	c. inherit	d. heredity
2. _____	a. nullify	b. annul	c. nullification	d. nullah
3. _____	a. infidelity	b. perfidy	c. affiliate	d. faithful
4. _____	a. insecure	b. sequel	c. ensue	d. consecutive
5. _____	a. trillion	b. terminate	c. tertiary	d. tricycle
6. _____	a. dozen	b. dual	c. double	d. dulcet
7. _____	a. deceiver	b. deception	c. decent	d. deceit
8. _____	a. dilatory	b. diligence	c. diligent	d. predilection
9. _____	a. allowance	b. laudable	c. laud	d. applaud
10. _____	a. satisfaction	b. satirical	c. satisfy	d. satiate

▶ EXERCISE 3

Decline the following phrase.

imperātor ācerrimus

	Singular	**Plural**
Nominative	_______________	_______________
Genitive	_______________	_______________
Dative	_______________	_______________
Accusative	_______________	_______________
Ablative	_______________	_______________
Vocative	_______________	_______________

▶ EXERCISE 4

Fill in the blanks with the correct form and degree of the adjective or adverb in parentheses.

Example: ___Doctissimīs___ hominibus praemia dare dēbēmus. (doctus superlative)

1. Verba fīliae tertiae ______________ erant quam aliārum fīliārum dicta. (vērus comparative)
2. Saepius ("more often") librōs ______________ quam librōs ______________ legere solēmus. (brevis comparative/longus comparative)
3. Nēmō est ______________ quam dux miserōrum. (miser comparative)
4. In hāc viā ambulābis ______________. (tūtus superlative)
5. Nihil est ______________ hōc venēnō. (fūnestus comparative)
6. Dē hīs cōnsiliīs ______________ iūdicāre dēbēmus. (celeriter; the adjective is celer, celeris, celere superlative)

▶ EXERCISE 5

Translate into English.

1. Pater igitur fīliam tertiam vehementissimē laudāvit quae patrem nōn tam vehementer laudāverat.

   ____

2. Postquam hostēs sunt victī, imperātor in imperium est celerrimē restitūtus.

   ____

3. Cicero amīcum fidēliōrem quam Atticum nōn habuit.

   ____

4. Verba fīliae prīmae Theodosiō dulcissima vidēbantur.

   ____

5. Iūstissimī hominēs rēs vērissimās occultāre nōn cupiunt.

   ____

6. In viā breviōre nōn longiōre ambulēmus.

   ____

Sir Henry Irving (1838–1905) became the first actor to be knighted for his achievements in 1895. He appeared in over five hundred roles in his half century on the stage including five tours through the United States. This image of Irving as Lear is from the program for *King Lear,* which Irving himself produced at the Lyceum Theatre, London.

▶ EXERCISE 6

Translate into Latin.

1. "I esteem you, father," said the daughter, "more deeply ('vehemently') than myself."

____

2. "You seem to me, daughter," said the father, "to be more loyal than <my> other daughters."

____

3. Of all the words, which the father had heard, these were the truest.

____

4. We ought to hear with a very unbiased attitude all things which are true.

____

5. The war is very deadly but our citizens are extremely brave.

____

6. Hatred is most foreign to me.

____

▶ EXERCISE 7

Read the following questions. Choose the best answer for each question and translate both the question and the selected answer. The questions pertain to the chapter reading passage.

quālis, quāle? – what sort of?

quōmodo? – in what way?, how?

Example: Cūr Theodosius imperātor fīliam nātū maximam dedit rēgī omnium praeclārissimō?

Fīlia nātū maxima dīxit sē patrem vehementius quam sē dīligere.

Theodosius imperātor Rōmānus clārissimus trēs fīliās pulcherrimās habuit.

Fīlia nātū maxima patrem vehementius quam sē dīlēxit.

Why did emperor Theodosius give his oldest daughter to the most distinguished king of all?
Fīlia nātū maxima dīxit sē patrem vehementius quam sē dīligere.
The oldest daughter said she esteemed her father more than herself.

1. Quālem marītum fīlia imperātōris secunda accēpit?

   Fīliae secundae verba imperātōrī satis bene placuērunt.

   Fīlia secunda tantum patrem dīlēxit quantum sē.

   Theodosius fīliam secundam cuidam ducī dedit.

   ____

   ____

   ____

2. Quōmodo Theodosius verba fīliae tertiae accēpit?

   Theodosius fīliam tertiam rogāvit quantum patrem dīligeret.

   Theodosius fīliam tertiam cuidam equitī dedit.

   Fīliae tertiae verba imperātōrī nōn valdē placuērunt.

   ____

   ____

   ____

3. Cūr Theodosius auxilium ā fīliābus petīvit?

   Theodosius trēs fīliās habēbat.

   Theodosius ad fīliam nātū maximam scrīpsit, ut auxilium ab eā peteret.

   Theodosiō ē terrīs suīs fugere necesse erat.

   ____

   ____

   ____

4. Cūr fīlia tertia hērēs imperātōris tandem facta est?

   Fīlia prīma tantum quīnque mīlitēs ex exercitū marītī ad patrem mīsit.

   Fīlia secunda respondit patrem posse apud sē et marītum habitāre et cibum et vestīmenta habēre, sed nihil aliud prōmīsit.

   Fīlia tertia ūnā cum marītō exercitum magnum parāvit, quem contrā hostēs imperātōris dūxit.

   ____

   ____

   ____

CONTENT QUESTIONS

After completing Chapter 6, answer these questions.

1. Why were collections of fables important in medieval Latin literature?

   ____

2. What was the approximate date of the *Gesta Rōmānōrum*?

   ____

3. To what declension do the endings of the comparative adjectives belong?

   ____

4. How are comparative adverbs formed?

   ____

5. When is the ablative of comparison not used?

   ____

6. How is the part of a whole expressed with the superlative?

   ____

CHAPTER 7

▶ EXERCISE 1

The verb *cupiō* has a meaning similar to that of the verb *volō*. Change the following forms of *cupiō* into forms of *volō*, the forms of *nōn cupiō* to the forms of *nōlō*, and the forms of *magis cupiō* ("rather want") to the forms of *mālō*.

1. cupiēbam ______________________
2. cupiēs ______________________
3. magis cupīvimus ______________________
4. nōn cupere ______________________
5. cupis ______________________
6. magis cupit ______________________
7. cupīvisse ______________________
8. magis cupīverātis ______________________
9. nōn cupīverint ______________________
10. nōn cupimus ______________________
11. nōn cupitis ______________________
12. magis cupīvērunt ______________________
13. nōn cupiēbat ______________________
14. cupīveram ______________________

▶ EXERCISE 2

For each derivative presented, choose the meaning of the Latin word from which the English is derived.

1. eternal	_____	a. year	b. age	c. and	d. always
2. fealty	_____	a. strong	b. treaty	c. faith	d. happy
3. vainglorious	_____	a. darkness	b. halo	c. pomp	d. glory
4. illumination	_____	a. light	b. threshold	c. moon	d. slippery
5. negotiate	_____	a. buyer	b. burden	c. license	d. leisure
6. confusion	_____	a. bottom	b. establish	c. pour	d. funeral
7. portrait	_____	a. trust	b. decorate	c. trial	d. drag
8. malevolent	_____	a. prefer	b. want	c. fly	d. strengthen
9. suborn	_____	a. embellished	b. desired	c. free	d. mouth
10. omnipotent	_____	a. drink	b. possess	c. possible	d. powerful
11. publicity	_____	a. tavern	b. common	c. edit	d. attract
12. qualify	_____	a. what sort	b. ask	c. how great	d. complain
13. etude	_____	a. music	b. exercise	c. study	d. safe
14. utensil	_____	a. burn	b. cook	c. metal	d. useful
15. onion	_____	a. sharp	b. one	c. burden	d. every
16. ubiquitous	_____	a. where	b. place	c. what sort	d. so many

▶ EXERCISE 3

Change the following imperatives into negative imperatives, using both ways of forming the negative imperative which you have learned. Translate the negative forms.

Example: laudā! nōlī laudāre! nē laudāveris! do not praise!

1. aedificā! ______________________________
2. cade! ______________________________
3. fundite! ______________________________
4. trahe! ______________________________
5. dēcipe! ______________________________
6. restituite! ______________________________
7. bibe! ______________________________
8. ōrā! ______________________________

▶ EXERCISE 4

Translate into English.

1. Virī fortissimī et doctissimī memoriā colentur eōrum, quī posteā venient.

2. Cicero semper putābat sē iūstius agere quam aliōs hominēs.
   iūstius – adverb related to *iūstus, a, um*

3. Vidēturne tibi epistula Petrarcae pulchrior epistulīs Cicerōnis?

4. Quī est longissimus liber omnium quōs lēgistī?

5. Ea quae Cicero scrīpsit sunt vetustiōra librīs ā Petrarcā scrīptīs.

6. Petrarca putat hominēs dēbēre difficultātēs aequiōre animō accipere quam Cicero.

▶ EXERCISE 5

Translate into Latin.

1. What sort of person do you want to be?

2. I always preferred to live in leisure.

3. They wanted glory but did not want to be dragged into a war.

4. Then the most powerful people wanted to destroy the freedom.

5. I will always prefer to seek light, not darkness.

6. I always wanted, do want, and will want most vehemently to save the republic.

▶ EXERCISE 6

In the chapter reading passage you read Petrarch's letter to Cicero. Later, Petrarch wrote a second letter. Translate the following text, an adapted portion of the second letter.

Petrarca Cicerōnī salūtem dīcit.

Litterīs meīs, quās ad tē mīseram, fortasse es offēnsus. Nōlēbam tamen rēs ā tē scrīptās reprehendere, sed tantum vītam tuam. Nam ut homō vīxistī, ut ōrātor dīxistī, ut philosophus scrīpsistī. Tantum rogābam ut cōnstantiam quaererēs et ex bellīs fugerēs. Ō, Rōmānī sermōnis pater, cui omnēs grātiās agimus! Nam tū hunc sermōnem coluistī et ōrnātissimum fēcistī. Dēbēs scīre nōmen tuum esse nunc celeberrimum et librōs tuōs ā multīs hominibus legī. Haec scrībere volēbam ut tibi gaudium darem.

Valē, mī Cicero!

Cicero, Cicerōnis, *m.* – Cicero
grātiās agō – to thank
ō! (*interjection*) – oh!
offendō, ere, offendī, offēnsum – to offend
ōrātor, ōrātōris, *m.* – orator
Petrarca, ae, *m.* – Petrarch
philosophus, ī, *m.* – philosopher
sermō, sermōnis, *m.* – speech, language

▶ EXERCISE 7

In Petrarch's letter to Cicero you read about Cicero's death which Petrarch deemed unworthy of a philosopher. The text below loosely based on a story related by the historian Cassius Dio (second–third century CE) provides more information about Cicero's death. Cassius Dio lived in the Roman Empire but wrote in Greek.

Translate the text.

Postquam Cicero ab hostibus suīs est occīsus, eius caput et dextra manus sunt excīsa et in rōstrīs Rōmānīs posita ut ab omnibus vidērentur. Fulvia Antōniī uxor ibi erat et multa mala verba dē Cicerōne fundēbat. Tandem tamen putāvit fortasse hoc satis nōn esse. Fortissimō odiō mōta linguam ex ōre Cicerōnis trāxit et fībulā suā perfōdit. Tunc caput rogāvit ut tam multās tamque ācrēs ōrātiōnēs habēret quam vellet.

Mārcus Antōnius, ī, *m.* – Mark Antony, Cicero's political enemy, who was ultimately responsible for Cicero's murder by soldiers

Cicerō, Cicerōnis, *m.* – Cicero

excīdō, ere, excīdī, excīsum – to cut out/away

fībula, ae, *f.* – brooch, hairpin, clip

lingua, ae, *f.* – tongue

perfodiō, ere, fōdī, fossum – to perforate

rōstra, ōrum, *n. pl.* – rostra, a platform in the Roman forum from which orators spoke; its name is derived from the ships' beaks (*rōstrum, ī,* n. – beak) taken from naval battles which adorned the platform

vellet – an imperfect subjunctive indicating possibility

Official announcements, like the proscriptions, were published in the Forum Romanum. In Cicero's day, the rostra that would have been located by the triple arch in the left corner of the photograph served as a public speaking platform. Following his murder, Cicero's tongue and hands were displayed on the rostra.

BY THE WAY

After Julius Caesar was murdered by pro-senatorial conspirators in 44 BCE, Cicero did not hide his hostility to Mark Antony, Caesar's henchman. Indeed Cicero delivered a total of fourteen violent speeches against Antony, aimed at discrediting him and reducing his power. Antony, however, reconciled himself with Octavian, who was Caesar's legally recognized successor, and part of their agreement involved the proscription of their common enemies, among whom was Cicero. Proscription meant that the name of the "proscribed" (from the verb *prōscrībere*) person was published in a written list of people declared enemies of the state, and therefore stripped of citizenship. Rewards were offered for information leading to the death or capture of a proscribed person, and anyone who killed a proscribed person could keep part of the slain person's estate. Cicero's speeches against Antony were called *The Philippics* because they were modeled on the speeches of the Athenian orator Demosthenes delivered in the fourth century BCE against the ambitions of Philip, King of Macedon, father of Alexander the Great, as he pursued his relentless ambition to subdue the independent city-states of Greece (such as Athens itself) to his rule.

A neoclassical interpretation of Julius Caesar casts him in his toga, crowned with laurel leaves, and with an idealized gaze of solemnity befitting an emperor. His will named his nineteen-year-old grandnephew Octavian his heir.

CONTENT QUESTIONS

After completing Chapter 7, answer these questions.

1. When and where did the Renaissance begin? By what was it characterized?

   ____

2. Who was Petrarch and when did he live?

   ____

3. In what languages did Petrarch write?

   ____

4. How are the verbs *volō, nōlō,* and *mālō* related?

   ____

5. What are the two ways to make a negative command in Latin, and what is the difference between the two ways?

   ____

6. What are the two meanings of *vīs*?

   ____

CHAPTER 8

▶ EXERCISE 1

Decline the following adjective.

maior, maius (the comparative adjective of *magnus*)

Singular

	Masculine/Feminine	**Neuter**
Nominative	____________	____________
Genitive	____________	____________
Dative	____________	____________
Accusative	____________	____________
Ablative	____________	____________
Vocative	____________	____________

Plural

Nominative	____________	____________
Genitive	____________	____________
Dative	____________	____________
Accusative	____________	____________
Ablative	____________	____________
Vocative	____________	____________

▶ EXERCISE 2

Choose the word which is **NOT** derived from the same Latin root.

	a.	b.	c.	d.
1. _____	a. artifice	b. arable	c. inertia	d. artillery
2. _____	a. multilingual	b. linguistics	c. language	d. tongue
3. _____	a. plush	b. plurality	c. surplus	d. pluperfect
4. _____	a. ancient	b. antique	c. anchylose	d. antiquity
5. _____	a. majesty	b. mayonnaise	c. majority	d. mayor
6. _____	a. maximize	b. maximum	c. maxim	d. Maxwell
7. _____	a. meliorism	b. ameliorate	c. melee	d. meliority
8. _____	a. mint	b. minuet	c. minuscule	d. minute
9. _____	a. optimist	b. option	c. optimize	d. optimum
10. _____	a. repair	b. pejorative	c. impair	d. pejoration
11. _____	a. pessimism	b. pessimist	c. pest	d. pessimistic
12. _____	a. domination	b. domino	c. dominion	d. dome
13. _____	a. hortatory	b. horticulture	c. exhort	d. exhortation
14. _____	a. locomotion	b. soliloquy	c. elocution	d. colloquial
15. _____	a. repartee	b. participle	c. partition	d. reparation
16. _____	a. compatible	b. patience	c. appease	d. passive
17. _____	a. sequestration	b. sequence	c. segue	d. suitable
18. _____	a. revere	b. revert	c. reverence	d. irreverent
19. _____	a. suite	b. sequel	c. consecutive	d. quest

An antique engraving honors two of Rome's most accomplished historians: Livy who traces Rome's history from its founding and Sallust who wrote about the Catilinarian conspiracy and the war with Jugurtha in North Africa.

▶ EXERCISE 3

Conjugate the following verb in the imperfect indicative and subjunctive.

dominor, dominārī, dominātus sum

Indicative

	Singular	**Plural**
First person	________________	________________
Second person	________________	________________
Third person	________________	________________

Subjunctive

	Singular	**Plural**
First person	________________	________________
Second person	________________	________________
Third person	________________	________________

▶ EXERCISE 4

Conjugate the following verb in the pluperfect indicative and subjunctive.

loquor, loquī, locūtus sum

Indicative

	Singular	**Plural**
First person	________________	________________
Second person	________________	________________
Third person	________________	________________

Subjunctive

	Singular	**Plural**
First person	________________	________________
Second person	________________	________________
Third person	________________	________________

▶ EXERCISE 5

Translate into English.

1. Clādem quam pessimam passī Rōmānī contrā Gallōs pugnābant.

2. Ducēs fortissimōs secūtī urbem ē Gallīs cēpērunt.

3. Nihil melius est quam linguam Latīnam gentibus dedisse.

4. Nē urbem nostram ā Gallīs esse captam patiāmur!

5. Per linguam nostram in magnā parte orbis terrārum domināmur.

6. Hominibus meliōribus praemia, peiōribus autem nihil dare dēbēmus.

▶ EXERCISE 6

Translate into Latin.

1. people/men having suffered disaster

2. people/men having been asked about many things

3. people/men being about to ask about many things

4. people/men being about to endure/put up with many things

5. We respect those kings but we do not love them.

6. You (pl.) will follow the leader and you will come to the city.

7. We shall divide rewards among the soldiers but we shall receive nothing from them.

▶ EXERCISE 7

Translate the following questions. Choose the best answer for each question and translate. The questions pertain to the chapter reading passage.

quōmodo? – in what way? how?
secundum + *acc.* – according to
sententia, ae, *f.* – opinion
superior, superius – superior, higher

Example: Quibus rēbus Valla putat maiōrēs suōs (his own) fuisse superiōrēs quam aliās gentēs?

Antīquī hominēs propter beneficia hominibus data colēbantur tamquam deī.
Maiōrēs eius nōn sōlum imperiī sed etiam linguae prōpāgātiōne aliōs omnēs superāvērunt.
Cerēs laudābātur, quod frūmentum hominibus dederat.

In what ways does Valla think his ancestors were superior to other peoples?
Maiōrēs eius nōn sōlum imperiī sed etiam linguae prōpāgātiōne aliōs omnēs superāvērunt.
His ancestors surpassed all others in the propagation not only of <their> empire, but also of <their> language.

1. Cūr crēdit Valla linguam Latīnam esse optimam frūgem et vērē dīvīnam?

   Hāc linguā hominēs artēs līberālēs docēbant et discēbant.

   Omnēs in prōvinciīs Latīnē loquēbantur.

   Hominēs imperium Rōmānum prīdem abiēcērunt.

   ____

   ____

   ____

2. Secundum Vallae sententiam, quōmodo Italī hominēs adhūc in magnā parte orbis terrārum rēgnant?

   Multae gentēs linguam Latīnam omnī aurō meliōrem putāvērunt.

   Apud multās gentēs lingua Latīna adhūc dominātur.

   Hominēs imperium Rōmānum prīdem abiēcērunt.

   ____

   ____

   ____

3. Cūr, secundum Vallae sententiam, lingua Latīna est eō in statū quō ōlim Rōma capta ā Gallīs?

   Vērī Quirītēs sunt linguae Latīnae cultōrēs.

   Nēmō litterārum bonīque pūblicī studiōsus ā lacrimīs temperāre potest.

   Sīcut Rōma ōlim capta ā Gallīs, nunc lingua Latīna ā barbarīs est oppressa.

   ____

   ____

   ____

4. Quid facere dēbent Quirītēs ut lingua Latīna līberētur?
    Vallam sequī dēbēbunt quī exercitum in hostēs dūcet.
    Parentem litterārum ā Gallīs captam esse patī dēbēbunt.
    Ibi esse dēbēbunt ubicumque lingua Latīna dominātur.

CONTENT QUESTIONS

After completing Chapter 8, answer these questions.

1. Give two reasons why the humanists wanted to restore the norms of classical Latin in the international language of their time.

2. What does the term *ēlegantia* mean in Latin rhetoric?

3. What is the meaning when *quam* is used with a superlative?

4. What is the most distinctive feature of deponent verbs?

5. How is the perfect participle of deponent verbs distinctive?

6. In what way can the future participle and future infinitive of deponents be considered an exception to the general rules about deponents?

CHAPTER 9

▶ EXERCISE 1

The verb *gerō* has a meaning somewhat similar to that of the verb *ferō*. Change the following forms of *gerō* into forms of *ferō*.

1. gessī ____________________
2. geram ____________________
3. gesta sunt ____________________
4. gere ____________________
5. gerī ____________________
6. geritis ____________________
7. geris ____________________
8. gereris ____________________
9. gestus erit ____________________
10. gerēbāmus ____________________

▶ EXERCISE 2

Choose the correct word, which fits the sense of each sentence, from the word bank provided.

aural	niveous	facade	popular
grandiloquent	onerous	immoderate	vernal
ambitious	faculty	reiterative	graceful
refrigerator	humility	humidity	multilingualism
engineer	conative	annoying	ballet
glacier	dismissal	progressive	nix
itinerant	inference	laborious	
oral	facsimile	inclement	

1. Rodrigo had ____________________ surgery to correct a hearing problem.
2. A ____________________ keeps food cold.
3. An ____________________ is well-versed in various types of machines.
4. ____________________ weather is common in Wisconsin during the winter.
5. The ____________________ preacher traveled constantly to reach all his parishioners.
6. The ____________________ flowers were snowy-white.

7. The donkey's burdens were ________________.
8. The ________________ were talented and made learning easy.
9. The new pope is known for his ________________.
10. The slender girl was a ________________ dancer.
11. Arabic has a ________________ tense, which is like the imperfect in Latin denoting repetitive effort.
12. ________________ on the last day of the school term is a joyful occasion for all.
13. The term "fax" is a shortened form of ________________.
14. Congress has made a ________________ of respectability for what is clearly a debacle.
15. We watched in horror as the ________________ slipped down the mountainside.
16. Her ________________ gestures made it apparent she had had no guide to good decorum.
17. ________________ taxation proceeds on the ability to pay.
18. A correct ________________ leads to a logical conclusion.

▶ EXERCISE 3

Translate into Latin.

1. I became ________________
2. I will become ________________
3. let it become! ________________
4. I want to become ________________
5. they become ________________
6. you were becoming ________________
7. what will become? ________________
8. they had become ________________

▶ EXERCISE 4

Write the present active imperative second person singular of the following verbs. Translate the forms.

1. addō ____________ ____________
2. dēmittō ____________ ____________
3. ferō ____________ ____________
4. perveniō ____________ ____________
5. fundō ____________ ____________
6. faciō ____________ ____________
7. trahō ____________ ____________
8. dūcō ____________ ____________
9. nōlō ____________ ____________
10. dīcō ____________ ____________

▶ EXERCISE 5

Write in Latin the masculine singular, superlative degree of the following adjectives.

1. difficult ____________
2. keen, fierce ____________
3. good ____________
4. dissimilar ____________
5. similar ____________
6. big ____________
7. slender ____________
8. sweet ____________
9. low ____________
10. strong ____________
11. easy ____________
12. heavy ____________

▶ EXERCISE 6

In the letter about his difficult trip during the ice storm, Erasmus mentioned Ulixes (i.e., Latin for the Greek Odysseus) and his endless travels. In the following two passages, loosely based on Homer's *Odyssey* (in Greek) you will learn more about the adventures of Odysseus.

Translate into English.

Ulixēs amīcīque ad īnsulam nāvigāvērunt et in spēluncam intrāvērunt. In spēluncā caseum invēnērunt quem comēdērunt. Paulō posteā Cyclōps nōmine Polyphēmus cum ovibus suīs in spēluncam intrāvit et statim aliquot nautās dēvorāvit. Omnēs timēre coepērunt; putābant enim Cyclōpem sē quoque esse dēvorātūrum. Cyclōps Ulixem rogāvit quod nōmen ille habēret. Ulixēs respondit sē Nēminem vocārī. Deinde Ulixēs, quī valdē callidus erat, multum vīnī Cyclōpī dedit. Cyclōps iam somnō ferēbātur, cum Ulixēs oculum eius (5) pīlō igne calefactō perfōdit. Cyclōps clāmāre coepit et dīcere sē occīdī. Aliī Cyclōpēs, quī in proximīs īnsulīs vīvēbant, clāmāvērunt et rogāvērunt quis eum occīderet. Illīs Polyphēmus ita respondit: "Nēmō. Nēmō mē occīdit." "Bene, bene" dīxērunt tum Cyclōpēs. "Sī nēmō tē occīdit, vīvis." Itaque auxilium eī nōn tulērunt. Posteā Ulixēs amīcīque ex spēluncā fūgērunt pendentēs ex ventribus ovium. Nam Cyclōps nōn sinēbat ūllum hominem ex spēluncā ambulāre. Cum iam in nāve erant, Ulixēs superbiā lātus clāmāvit sē esse Ulixem (10) et Ulixem oculum Cyclōpis perfōdisse. Cyclōps hoc audīvit et īrā mōtus patrem suum Neptūnum, marium deum, rogāvit, ut ventīs Ulixis nāvem dēlēret. Iter Ulixis posteā fuit difficillimum.

The sixteenth-century Neptune Fountain stands in the Long Market of Gdańsk, Poland's major seaport. At the center of the city's social and commercial life, Neptune symbolizes the city's special relationship with the sea. Gdańsk was a member of the Hanseatic League and in its shipbuilding yards the twentieth-century Solidarity movement was born.

aliquot (*adv.*) – a few

calefactus, a, um – heated

callidus, a, um – smart, shrewd

caseus, ī, *m.* – cheese

clāmō, āre, āvī, ātum – to shout

Cyclōps, Cyclōpis, *m.* – Cyclops, a giant with one eye in the center of his forehead

dēvorō, āre, āvī, ātum – to devour

multum + *partitive genitive* – a lot of

Neptūnus, ī, *m.* – Neptune

ovis, ovis, *f.* – sheep

pendēns, pendentis – hanging

perfodiō, ere, perfōdī, perfossum – to pierce through

pīlum, ī, *n.* – staff

superbia, ae, *f.* – pride

Ulixēs, Ulixis, *m.* – Ulysses

venter, ventris, *m.* – belly

Aeolus, king of the winds, was not the least empathetic when Odysseus returned again seeking help after his comrades had released the winds from the bag which the king had previously given him. Homer's stories similar to this one served as a moral guide for the ancient Greeks.

▶ EXERCISE 7

Translate into Latin.

The god of the winds had given Ulysses a bag so that it might be saved by him. Ulysses always carried the bag with himself and did not allow the other sailors to touch it. They had sailed a very long way and were almost at home. The trip was very easy; in fact, the winds were very good. The sailors, however, thought that Ulysses had hidden riches in the bag. Therefore, while Ulysses was sleeping, they opened the bag. What happened then? Very strong winds began to blow everywhere. The ship, on which Ulysses and his friends were, was carried far away from their fatherland.

____

____

____

____

____

____

____

____

____

auferō, auferre, abstulī, ablātum – to carry away
flō, flāre, flāvī, flātum – to blow
sarcina, ae, *f.* – bag
sēcum = cum sē – with herself/himself/itself
Ulixēs, Ulixis, *m.* – Ulysses

CONTENT QUESTIONS

After completing Chapter 9, answer these questions.

1. Who was Erasmus, when did he live, and what was his nationality?

____

____

2. What kind of works did Erasmus write?

____

3. How did Erasmus feel about limiting one's use of the Latin language to the language of Cicero only?

____

____

4. What are the meanings of the verb *fīō*?

____

5. What do the verbs *ferō* and *faciō* have in common?

____

6. Which adjectives form their superlative degree using the suffix –*limus*?

____

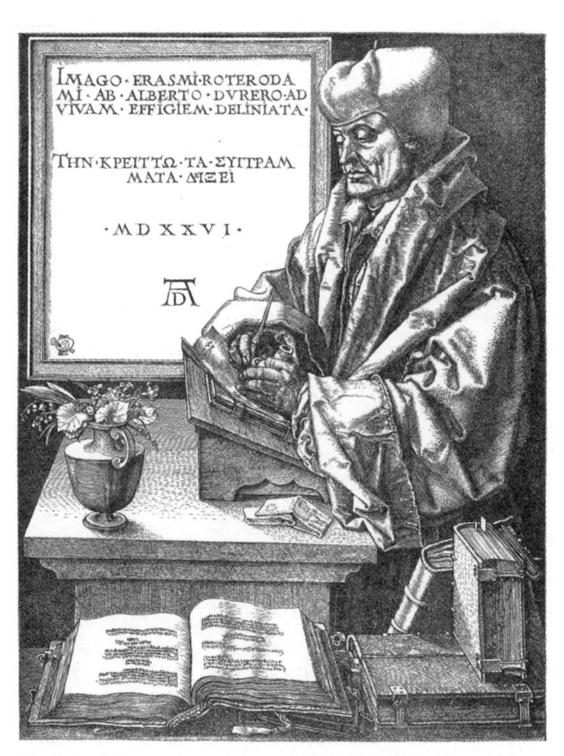

The famed Renaissance artist, German Albrecht Dürer (1471–1528) had sketched Erasmus over the course of a few meetings in 1520 and 1521 and executed this engraving in 1526. Dürer surrounded Erasmus with his books to celebrate the humanist's intellectual prowess. The inscriptions in both Latin and Greek also attest to Erasmus's scholarship.

CHAPTER 10

▶ EXERCISE 1

Change the following to forms of *eō* keeping the same person, number, tense, mood, and voice.

1. ambulāvimus ____________________
2. ambulāveritis ____________________
3. ambulābunt ____________________
4. ambulās ____________________
5. ambulābātis ____________________
6. ambulāverās ____________________
7. ambulātum est ____________________
8. ambulāre ____________________
9. ambulābis ____________________
10. ambulēmus ____________________
11. ambulāvissēs ____________________

▶ EXERCISE 2

Determine which of the following is derived from the Latin word provided.

1. *aedēs*	____	a. edible	b. educate	c. edifice	d. editor
2. *labor*	____	a. labial	b. laboratory	c. labiate	d. labyrinth
3. *lūcrum*	____	a. pellucid	b. reluctance	c. collusion	d. lucre
4. *modus*	____	a. remodel	b. meddle	c. demean	d. subdue
5. *pecūnia*	____	a. impeccable	b. impecunious	c. pectoral	d. peculiar
6. *suī*	____	a. suite	b. suitor	c. suitable	d. suicide
7. *iūcundus*	____	a. young	b. enjoin	c. jocund	d. injunction
8. *liber*	____	a. deliver	b. deliberate	c. libation	d. libelous
9. *maritimus*	____	a. merisis	b. maritime	c. meritocracy	d. marital
10. *placidus*	____	a. place	b. placket	c. placenta	d. placid

11. *prosperus* _____ a. prospect b. prosopopoeia c. prosperity d. prospectus

12. *serēnus* _____ a. serenade b. discern c. serious d. serendipity

13. *furor* _____ a. furtive b. furrow c. suffer d. infuriate

14. *eō* _____ a. inefficient b. initiate c. erratic d. impromptu

15. *laedō* _____ a. lagoon b. collusion c. collision d. languish

▶ EXERCISE 3

Fill in the blanks with the correct form of *suī, sibi, sē, sē*. Translate each sentence.

Example: Amōre ___suī___ saepe dēcipiuntur hominēs.
Men are often deceived by love of self.

1. Dīxit dōnum illud __________ placēre.

 ____

2. Dīxit __________ illud dōnum tibi dedisse.

 ____

3. Dīxērunt __________ in illā viā per nivēs et glaciem Rōmam itūrōs esse.

 ____

4. Haec omnia ā __________ esse aliēna putant.

 ____

5. Cicero cīvēs Rōmānōs futūrōs esse __________ immemorēs nōn crēdēbat.

 ____

6. Cicero ōrātiōnem Atticī __________ placēre dīxit.

 ____

▶ EXERCISE 4

Fill in the following blanks with either the correct genitive of *is, ea, id* or the appropriate form of *suus* based on the clue provided in parentheses. Translate each sentence.

Example: Ad aedēs __eius__ nōn semel īvit Erasmus. (amīcus Erasmī aedēs possidet)
Erasmus went to his (someone else's) house not once.

1. Ad aedēs ________ nōn semel īvērunt nautae. (nautae aedēs possident)

   ____

2. Ad aedēs ________ nōn semel īvērunt nautae. (Erasmus aedēs possidet)

   ____

3. Amīcō ________ valēdīcere (*say goodbye*) voluit Erasmus. (amīcus est Erasmī)

   ____

4. Amīcō ________ valēdīcere voluit Erasmus. (amīcus est nautārum)

   ____

5. Amīcō ________ valēdīcere voluit Erasmus. (amīcus est Thomae Morī)

   ____

6. Erasmus sē ________ librōs habēre crēdēbat. (librī sunt Erasmī)

   ____

7. Erasmus sē ________ librōs habēre crēdēbat. (librī sunt rēgīnārum)

   ____

8. Erasmus sē ________ librōs habēre crēdēbat. (librī sunt Thomae Morī)

   ____

While in Basle, Erasmus befriended the painter Holbein whose work he recommended to Thomas More and his other English friends. This portrait copied from a woodcut attests to Holbein's mastery of the medium. Holbein's engravings served as illustrations for Martin Luther's German translation of the Bible and for *The Praise of Folly* by Erasmus.

▶ EXERCISE 5

Change the plural sentences into the singular and vice versa. Translate the changed sentences.

Example: Rēgēs illī nautās suōs scelestōs laudāre nōn dēbent.
Rēx ille nautam suum scelestum laudāre nōn dēbet.
That king ought not to praise his (own) wicked sailor.

1. Nauta putat hunc hominem sibi invidēre.

____

____

2. Nautae putant sē eōrum librōs fūrātūrōs esse.

____

____

3. Hic cīvis sē suam sarcinam ē nautā scelestō numquam receptūrum esse crēdēbat.

____

____

4. Nauta iubet vectōrem sibi sarcinam dare.

____

____

▶ EXERCISE 6

Translate into English.

1. Soror mea tēcum stābit.

____

2. Nautae, quibuscum nāvigāre dēbēbam, fūrēs erant scelestissimī.

____

3. Hoc iter, nautae, vōbīscum facere nōlō.

____

4. Illī nautae sēcum sarcinās suās ferre dēbent.

____

5. Poēta mēcum manēbat ut librōs ūnā legere possēmus.

____

6. Ad aedēs amīcī, quōcum loquī cupiēbam, nōn semel īvī.

____

▶ EXERCISE 7

Translate into Latin.

1. I shall go with all of you (pl.).

2. If only you (pl.) would go with us!

3. It was necessary for me to go with them.

4. He realized that it was necessary for him(self) to go with me.

5. That man, who was going with you, had wanted to go with me.

6. If only we had gone with you (pl.)!

CONTENT QUESTIONS

After completing Chapter 10, answer these questions.

1. What effect did the visits of Erasmus to England have on the culture of the English?

2. For what special reason did Erasmus think the Kings of England (of the English) should take action against sailors who behaved like robbers?

3. Which is the shortest sentence in Latin?

4. What is the most fundamental difference between the reflexive third person pronoun *suī, sibi, sē, sē* and other demonstratives of the third person?

5. What is the difference between singular and plural forms of the third person reflexive pronoun?

6. How does the meaning of the genitive of the third person reflexive pronoun differ from the meaning of the genitive of other non-reflexive third person demonstratives?

CHAPTER 11

▶ EXERCISE 1

Decline the present active participles of the following verbs.

1. *salūtō, salūtāre, salūtāvī, salūtātum*

		Singular	
	Masculine	**Feminine**	**Neuter**
Nominative	______	______	______
Genitive	______	______	______
Dative	______	______	______
Accusative	______	______	______
Ablative	______	______	______
Vocative	______	______	______
		Plural	
Nominative	______	______	______
Genitive	______	______	______
Dative	______	______	______
Accusative	______	______	______
Ablative	______	______	______
Vocative	______	______	______

2. *nesciō, nescīre, nescīvī, nescītum*

	Masculine	Singular Feminine	Neuter
Nominative	______	______	______
Genitive	______	______	______
Dative	______	______	______
Accusative	______	______	______
Ablative	______	______	______
Vocative	______	______	______
		Plural	
Nominative	______	______	______
Genitive	______	______	______
Dative	______	______	______
Accusative	______	______	______
Ablative	______	______	______
Vocative	______	______	______

▶ EXERCISE 2

Determine which of the following is **NOT** derived from the Latin word provided.

1. *gemma* _____ a. gemniporous b. gemmate c. Gemma d. Gemini
2. *legātus* _____ a. legate b. legation c. legato d. legatee
3. *populus* _____ a. poplar b. pueblo c. people d. population
4. *servus* _____ a. dessert b. severe c. serf d. sergeant
5. *alter* _____ a. alteration b. altruistic c. alto d. adulterate
6. *neuter* _____ a. neutron b. neutralize c. neuter d. neuron
7. *nūllus* _____ a. nuclear b. annul c. nullify d. nullipara
8. *sōlus* _____ a. desolate b. console c. sullen d. solitaire
9. *tōtus* _____ a. totalitarian b. factotum c. tote d. total
10. *nesciō* _____ a. nescience b. nice c. nicely d. niche
11. *salūtō* _____ a. salubrious b. salutary c. salutatorian d. salutation
12. *spectō* _____ a. spectator b. specific c. spectrology d. spectacles

13. *taceō* _____ a. reticence b. taciturn c. tacit d. retinue

14. *ūtor* _____ a. perusal b. abusive c. combustible d. usury

15. *minimē* _____ a. miniature b. minimize c. minimum d. minimal

▶ EXERCISE 3

Fill in the blanks using the correct form of *alius, alter, neuter, nūllus, sōlus, tōtus, ūllus, ūnus,* or *uter.*

Example: Numquam ___ūlla___ rēs fuit mihi difficilior.
Never was any thing more difficult to me.

1. __________ homō aurum, argentum, et dīvitiās tam multum amāre dēbet.

   ____

2. __________ cōnsul alterum exspectāre volēbat.

   ____

3. __________ coniugum domum magis cūrat?

   ____

4. Difficile est vīvere __________ hominī sine amīcīs.

   ____

5. __________ mente dē tē cōgitō.

   ____

6. Numquam __________ homō mē fēlicior fuit.

   ____

7. __________ rem sciō: mē nihil scīre.

   ____

8. Ego nihil faciam; __________ facere poterunt.

   ____

Woodcut from Thomas More's *Ūtopia* shows More at the center in discussion with his fictional character Raphael Hythlodaeus (Hythloday), traveler and philosopher. To More's right is Petrus Aegidius (Peter Giles), Antwerp humanist to whom More was introduced by their mutual friend Erasmus. On the left is Iohannes Clemēns (John Clement), President of the College of Physicians and tutor to More's children.

▶ EXERCISE 4

Translate the following text adapted from an excerpt from the second book of *Ūtopia*.

Quattuor hospitia maxima sunt extrā urbem sita parvīs oppidīs similia. Ibi plurimīs aegrōtīs est locus nec ūllus homō, quī nōn valet, in urbe iacēre solet. Hoc fit nē contāgiō ab aliō ad alium hominem serpat. Hospitia omnia habent quae habēre necesse est; medicī doctissimī atque hūmānissimī aegrōtōs optimē cūrant. Nēmō igitur aegrōtus māvult domī manēre quam ad hospitium ferrī.

____

____

____

____

____

____

____

____

aegrōtus, a, um – sick
alius . . . alius . . . – one . . . another . . .
contāgiō, contāgiōnis, *f.* – contagion
hospitium, ī, *n.* – guesthouse
medicus, ī, *m.* – doctor
oppidum, ī, *n.* – town
optimē – superlative of *bene*
quattuor (*number*) – four
serpō, ere, serpsī, — – to creep, spread

▶ EXERCISE 5

Fill in the blanks with the correct form of the participle. The vocabulary supplied in Exercise 4 may be consulted. Translate the sentences.

Example: Dē hospitiīs ____legēns____ multa didicī. (legō)
<While> reading about the guesthouses I learned many things.

1. Ūtopiēnsēs bona hospitia ____________ aegrōtōs suōs bene cūrāre nec neglegere videntur. (habeō)
   Ūtopiēnsis, Ūtopiēnsis, *m.* – Utopian

   ____

2. Ūtopiēnsēs hominēs nōn bene ____________ in hospitium ferre dēbēbant nec sinere eōs domī manēre. (valeō)

   ____

   ____

3. Perīcula venīre poterant ex hominibus aegrōtīs in urbe ____________ et domī ____________.
   (maneō, iaceō)

   ____

4. Lībertās hominum ibi ____________ nōn semper maxima vidētur. (vīvō)

   ____

▶ EXERCISE 6

Translate the text adapted from an excerpt from the second book of *Ūtopia.*

Hominī diplōma ā prīncipe datum nōn habentī nōn licet urbis fīnēs relinquere. Ūtopiēnsēs ex urbe fugientēs capiuntur et tamquam servī ad urbem dūcuntur. Nam cupientēs extrā fīnēs ambulāre coniugem et patrem rogāre dēbent ut sē hoc facere sinant. Cum ad locum ubi hominēs habitant pervenerint, ab hōrīs mātūtīnīs ad merīdiem labōribus darī dēbēbunt. Iter facientibus nōn est necesse cibum sēcum ferre. Nam ubīque sine ūllā pecūniā datā post labōrēs cibum accipiunt.

____

____

____

____

____

____

____

____

____

____

diplōma, diplōmatis, *n.* – passport (with an exit visa)
hōrīs mātūtīnīs – the morning hours
prīnceps, prīncipis, *m.* – chief
Ūtopiēnsis, Ūtopiēnsis, *m.* – Utopian

▶ EXERCISE 7

Translate into Latin. Each sentence requires a participle.

1. To no man not owning a passport is it allowed to make a trip.
   diplōma, diplōmatis, *n.*

   ____

2. The trips of the people dwelling there ought to be short.

   ____

3. The father and the spouse ought to allow the <people> desiring to walk to make a trip.

   ____

4. Men and women cultivating the fields will receive food.

   ____

5. Don't carry food with you <while> making a trip!

   ____

A Victorian artist's interpretation of Anne Boleyn. When Catherine of Aragón did not bear Henry VIII a surviving male heir, he sought an annulment of the marriage so that he could marry Anne Boleyn. Thomas More maintained his loyalty to the pope who denied Henry's request. For her later alleged adultery, Boleyn, who did not produce a male heir either, was executed.

CONTENT QUESTIONS

After completing Chapter 11, answer these questions.

1. Who was Thomas More, when did he live, and how did he die?

____

____

2. What is Thomas More's most important work and what does its name mean?

____

3. What participles in Latin do you know so far; and what is the difference between them?

____

____

____

____

4. How is the present participle formed?

____

____

____

____

5. Which are the nine adjectives with genitive in *–īus* and dative in *–ī*?

____

6. Where else have you encountered the genitive ending *–ius* (or *–īus*) and dative *–i* (or *–ī*)?

____

Catherine Parr married Henry VIII on July 12th, 1543, at Hampton Court Palace. She was the first English Queen Consort to enjoy the new title "Queen of Ireland" following Henry's adoption of the title "King of Ireland." As queen, Catherine was much beloved by his daughters from his first two marriages, who would later rule as Queens Mary and Elizabeth.

CHAPTER 12

▶ EXERCISE 1

Translate the following conjunctions into Latin. Sometimes more than one answer is possible.

1. after ____________________________
2. and ____________________________
3. although ____________________________
4. however ____________________________
5. if ____________________________
6. while ____________________________
7. when ____________________________
8. because ____________________________
9. but ____________________________
10. as soon as ____________________________
11. unless ____________________________
12. as often as ____________________________

▶ EXERCISE 2

Match the derivative in Column A to the meaning of its Latin source in Column B. Some meanings may be used more than once; some not at all.

	Column A		Column B
1. _____	cherish	A.	approve
2. _____	officer	B.	lot
3. _____	exorbitant	C.	dear
4. _____	sententious	D.	die
5. _____	consort	E.	circle
6. _____	caress	F.	nevertheless
7. _____	mortgage	G.	duty
8. _____	probably	H.	sentence
9. _____	despair	I.	hope
10. _____	sorcerer	J.	too much
11. _____	officious	K.	if not
12. _____	charity		
13. _____	mortification		
14. _____	proof		
15. _____	assorted		

▶ EXERCISE 3

Combine the following pairs of sentences into a complex sentence using a temporal clause. Include a temporal conjunction and, if needed, change the mood and tense. Translate the changed sentence.

1. Colōnus dē terrīs novīs audīvit. Nāvēs parāre cupīvit.

   Colōnus, ī, *m.* – Columbus

   ____

   ____

2. Ē rēgibus Lūsitānōrum et Britannōrum auxilium petīvit. Illī auxilium dare nōluērunt.

   Lūsitānus, ī, *m.* – Portuguese **Britannus, ī,** *m.* – British

   ____

   ____

   ____

   ____

3. Rēx et rēgīna Hispānōrum audiēbant ea quae Colōnus dīcēbat. Intellegēbant rem esse magnam.

   Hispānus, ī, *m.* – Spaniard

4. Colōnus ex rēge et rēgīnā Hispānōrum pecūniam accēpit. Statim nāvēs parāre coepit.

The engraving shows a young Ferdinand of Aragón who served as king not only of Spain but also of Sicily and Naples. Ferdinand known as "the Catholic" ruled jointly with his wife Isabella.

▶ EXERCISE 4

Change the sentence *Sī nāvis mihi datur, nāvigō,* in order to construct an example of each of the six types of condition. Translate each.

This engraving presents a montage of images from Columbus's voyage. In the lower left-hand corner, King Ferdinand of Spain gives instructions with his pointed finger, in the center sail two of Columbus's ships while from the third men disembark and meet the indigenous peoples of the island.

▶ EXERCISE 5

Translate into Latin.

1. Columbus was seeking help and money because he wanted to look for and find a new land.

2. Many kings did not want to give him money because the undertaking (*rēs*) was difficult and could lead to nothing.

3. Only the king and queen of the Spaniards approved of his opinion because in that undertaking (*rēs*) there was a very great hope.
   Hispānus, ī, *m.* – Spaniard

4. Then Columbus began to prepare ships and sailors because he had money.

▶ EXERCISE 6

Combine the following pairs of sentences into a complex sentence using either causal or concessive clauses. Include the correct conjunctions and, if needed, change the mood and tense. Translate the changed sentence.

1. Colōnus sciēbat esse terrās novās. Hoc ab aliō nautā audīverat.

2. Omnēs dīcunt Colōnum prīmum terrās novās invēnisse. Alius ante eum viam ad illās terrās invēnerat.

3. Plūrimī rēgēs nōluērunt Colōnō pecūniam ad iter dare. Poterant maximum imperium et dīvitiās ex illō itinere accipere.

4. Rēx et rēgīna Hispānōrum magnum imperium et magnās dīvitiās accēpērunt. Illī Colōnō auxilium dedērunt et Colōnus novās terrās invenīre potuit.

▶ EXERCISE 7

Some years after the discovery of America by Columbus, another Italian, from the city of Florence, by the name of Amerigo Vespucci, sailed along the shores of both South and North America. Afterward he wrote a letter in Latin entitled *Mundus novus* to the rulers of Florence. In 1507 German cartographers, one of which was Martin Waldeseemüller, published a map of the world with updates based on the new discoveries (the original is now in the Library of Congress in Washington, DC).

Translate the paragraph adapted from the map text. Then translate the related sentences.

In mente habēmus tōtum orbem terrārum dēscrībere. Trēs partēs sunt bene ostentae et etiam quarta pars ab Americō Vesputiō inventa. Nōn intellegō quis possit nōn sinere eam hūius virī fortissimī nōmine vocārī, id est Americam tamquam Americī terram. Nam Europa et Asia ā mulieribus nōmina sua accēpērunt.

America, ae, *f.* – America

Americus Vesputius, ī, *m.* – Amerigo Vespucci (sometimes called *Vespuccius*)

Asia, ae, *f.* – Asia

dēscrībō, ere, dēscrīpsī, dēscrīptum – to describe

Eurōpa, ae, *f.* – Europe (Europa was a young girl loved by Jupiter who had disguised himself as a bull).

id est – i.e. (that is)

quartus, a, um – fourth

1. Quamquam Colōnus Americam invēnit, hōc locō Vesputius dīcitur Americam invēnisse.

2. Orbis terrārum modō novō dēscrībī dēbēbat quia novae terrae erant inventae.

3. Sī virī fortissimī nōn nāvigāvissent, novus orbis nōn esset nōbīs apertus.

4. Cum prīmī, quī ad terrās novās nāvigāverant, Americam invēnissent, multī aliī eōs sunt secūtī. Rēs illīs erant prosperae.

CONTENT QUESTIONS

After completing Chapter 12, answer these questions.

1. Who was Sepúlveda and when did he live?

2. What is the title of Sepúlveda's main work, and what is it about?

3. Which conjunctions introduce temporal clauses and what moods do they require?

4. Which conjunctions introduce causal clauses and what moods do they require?

5. Which conjunctions introduce concessive clauses and what moods do they require?

6. Which conjunctions introduce conditional clauses and what moods do they require?

CHAPTER 13

▶ EXERCISE 1

Decline the following phrase.

īdem nauta

	Singular	Plural
Nominative	______________	______________
Genitive	______________	______________
Dative	______________	______________
Accusative	______________	______________
Ablative	______________	______________

▶ EXERCISE 2

Choose the meaning of the Latin word from which the English word is derived.

1. benevolence	_____	a. blessing	b. farewell	c. goodwill	d. softhearted
2. multitudinous	_____	a. crowd	b. varied	c. several	d. people
3. socialize	_____	a. sun	b. pack	c. slave	d. ally
4. turret	_____	a. defense	b. tower	c. end	d. crowd
5. venial	_____	a. sale	b. vein	c. pardon	d. wind
6. verge	_____	a. spring	b. edge	c. fear	d. stick
7. volunteer	_____	a. will	b. fly	c. turn	d. pleasure
8. retaliation	_____	a. hold back	b. such	c. slow	d. return
9. declare	_____	a. shout	b. shut down	c. reveal	d. retard
10. irascible	_____	a. be angry	b. mock	c. rub	d. provoke
11. mirror	_____	a. image	b. look at	c. ghost	d. admire
12. renegade	_____	a. business	b. deny	c. leisure	d. neither
13. supernumerary	_____	a. excess	b. divinity	c. count	d. naïve
14. offensive	_____	a. come upon	b. hateful	c. attack	d. mistake
15. referee	_____	a. report	b. fair	c. judge	d. cruel
16. identity	_____	a. self	b. same	c. perfect	d. name

▶ EXERCISE 3

Decline the following phrases.

1. *rēgīna ipsa*

	Singular	Plural
Nominative	______	______
Genitive	______	______
Dative	______	______
Accusative	______	______
Ablative	______	______

2. *cōnsilium istud*

	Singular	Plural
Nominative	______	______
Genitive	______	______
Dative	______	______
Accusative	______	______
Ablative	______	______

▶ EXERCISE 4

Translate into Latin.

1. Of the same islands.

______

2. I see the island itself.

______

3. Let us speak about those soldiers of yours!

______

4. Give me the same gifts which you gave before!

______

5. We saw the ship of the leader himself.

______

6. You yourself love yourself.

______

7. We ourselves marvel at those plans of yours.

______

▶ EXERCISE 5

Fill in the blanks with the correct form of *īdem* and translate into English.

Example: ___Eōsdem___ librōs amō atque tū.
I love the same books as you.

1. ______________ incolās cōnspicimus, quōs saepe vīderāmus.

____

2. In ______________ īnsulae parte sumus.

____

3. Nōn iam ______________ modō dē ______________ rēbus cōgitāmus, quō anteā (*before*).

____

4. Haec verba nōn sunt nova sed ______________ .

____

5. ______________ litterae sunt Colōnō datae.

____

6. ______________ in locō numquam manēmus.

____

▶ EXERCISE 6

Translate into English.

1. Colōnō sē in Hispāniam redīre dēbēre intellegente, aliī eum manēre volēbant.

____

2. Colōnō omnēs in Hispāniam redīre posse negante, aliī dē aliō cōnsiliō cōgitābant.

____

3. Vī dīvīnā in litterīs cōnspectā, incolae rem sacram tangere nōlēbant.

____

4. Paucissimīs Hispānīs in īnsulā relictīs, quid fiet?

____

5. Animō Colōnī hīs verbīs offēnsō, Martīnus in aliam īnsulae partem īvit.

____

6. Terrīs novīs iam inventīs, aliī Hispānī ūnā cum multīs mīlitibus et nāvibus venient.

____

▶ EXERCISE 7

Choose the answer that best fits each question and translate it into English. To answer the questions well, review the passage at the beginning of Chapter 13.

1. Cūr Colōnus in Hispāniam redīre voluit?

   Colōnus in Hispāniam redīre voluit ut aliōs Hispānōs ad eāsdem īnsulās dūceret.

   Colōnus in Hispāniam redīre voluit ut castra aedificāret.

   Colōnus in Hispāniam redīre voluit quia nōlēbat in terrā novā manēre.

   ____

   ____

2. Cūr Colōnus turrim ligneam aedificārī iussit?

   Colōnus turrim ligneam aedificārī iussit ut castra ibi pōnerentur.

   Colōnus turrim ligneam aedificārī iussit ut aliōs Hispānōs ad eāsdem īnsulās dūceret.

   Colōnus turrim ligneam aedificārī iussit quia Martīnī cōnsilia eī nōn placuērunt.

   ____

   ____

Based on Theodore de Bry's work, this illustration conflates several episodes into a single image: erecting a cross on the island Guanahari and receiving presents from the Caciques of Hispaniola in the foreground with the arrival of the ships, disembarking, landing, and frightening the indigenous peoples in the background.

3. Cūr incolae vim dīvīnam in epistulīs esse putāvērunt?

Incolae vim dīvīnam in epistulīs esse putāvērunt quia Colōnum nōn amābant.

Incolae vim dīvīnam in epistulīs esse putāvērunt quia vidērunt hominēs ex epistulīs cōnsilia aliōrum absentium intellegere.

Incolae vim dīvīnam in epistulīs esse putāvērunt quia eās ferre dēbēbant.

---

4. Cūr Martīnus cōnsilium Colōnī nōn probāvit?

Martīnus in Hispāniam redīre nōluit.

Martīnus paucōs Hispānōs relictōs, Colōnō et multīs aliīs absentibus, in magnō perīculō versārī posse putāvit.

Martīnus īrātus est et cum nōnnūllīs sociīs in aliam īnsulae partem discessit.

---

5. Cum aliī Colōnum hortātī essent, ut Martīnō veniam daret, quid fēcit Colōnus?

Colōnus nōnnūllōs Hispānōs in aliam īnsulae partem mīsit.

Colōnus epistulam ad Martīnum mīsit.

Colōnus īrātus est.

CONTENT QUESTIONS

After completing Chapter 13, answer these questions:

1. Why is the ablative absolute called "absolute"?

2. Of what other kinds of subordinate clauses can the ablative absolute be an equivalent?

3. What is the basic difference between the intensive pronoun/adjective and the reflexive pronoun?

4. What is the special meaning of *iste, ista, istud*?

5. Why was Martín Pinzón angered at Columbus's plan to leave some Spaniards in Hispaniola, while he (Columbus) sailed to Spain?

6. Why does Sepúlveda use the word *barbarī* to mean the inhabitants of the New World?

The commemoration of Columbus's exploration of the New World is celebrated with a federal holiday in the United States (second Monday in October). The holiday has, in turn, led to the creation of multiple images of Columbus like the one depicted.

CHAPTER 14

▶ EXERCISE 1

Give the supine in *–m* for each of the following.

1. affirmō ____________________
2. circumeō ____________________
3. numerō ____________________
4. contineō ____________________
5. redeō ____________________
6. volvō ____________________
7. referō ____________________
8. sentiō ____________________

Galileo made improvements upon the looking glass invented by the Dutch. By equipping it with high-powered lenses, he transformed it into the telescope that he presents to the Muses. Printmaker Stefano della Bella used artistic allegory in the frontispiece of this rare first edition of Galileo's *Opere* to communicate Galileo's proof that the earth revolves around the sun.

▶ EXERCISE 2

Choose the word that is derived from the same Latin root as the given word.

1. elementary ____ a. elephant b. eleemosynary c. elevate d. element
2. aggravate ____ a. ingratiate b. grief c. aggrandize d. segregate
3. automobile ____ a. mutineer b. morale c. mutation d. multiply
4. naturalist ____ a. renown b. renaissance c. renew d. reconnaissance
5. pound ____ a. compound b. expound c. ponder d. depot
6. quiescent ____ a. acquire b. conquest c. querulous d. requite
7. quotidian ____ a. diary b. quotient c. adieu d. quotation
8. commensurate ____ a. semester b. measure c. mention d. supereminent
9. infinitive ____ a. confiscate b. fiction c. paraffin d. affable
10. mediocre ____ a. medullary b. meditate c. medical d. mediate
11. confirm ____ a. affinity b. farm c. fertile d. afferent
12. circulate ____ a. research b. citation c. civilian d. reality
13. continent ____ a. contention b. contemporary c. contiguous d. continuous
14. revolution ____ a. voluptuary b. voluntary c. vault d. volatile
15. necessary ____ a. because b. unceasing c. scissors d. necrosis

▶ EXERCISE 3

Combine the following pairs of sentences into a complex sentence using the words in parentheses in the new main and subordinate clause. Change the tense and the mood of the verb in the subordinate clause as needed. Translate the changed sentences.

1. Pauca dē mundō antīquī sciēbant. Putābant terram nōn movērī. (tam, ut)

____

____

2. Per tot annōs hominēs putāre solēbant terram esse in mediā parte mundī. Difficile eīs fuit novam sententiam accipere. (ut)

____

____

____

____

3. Copernicus bene dē omnibus rēbus cōgitāvit. Intellēxit terram circum sōlem movērī. (tam, ita)

____

____

4. Galilēus crēdēbat Copernicum vēra cōgitāvisse. Nōluit sententiam eius reprehendere, quamquam est hāc dē causā pūnītus. (ita, ut)

____

____

____

____

5. Ea quae Copernicus et Galilēus affirmāvērunt sunt vēra. Eōrum sententiās etiam hodiē probāmus. (tam, ut)

____

____

▶ EXERCISE 4

Change the following clauses with *ut* into forms of the supine in –*m* expressing purpose. Translate the sentences.

1. Currō ut praemium capiam.

   ____

   ____

2. Circumeō aedēs ut librum meum inveniam.

   ____

   ____

3. Noctū ambulō ut caelum spectem.

   ____

   ____

4. Venī ut dē rērum nātūrā verba dīcās!

   ____

   ____

5. Nōlī īre ut sōlem spectēs!

   ____

   ____

6. Hī doctī convēnērunt ut dē mōtū terrae ōrātiōnem audīrent.

   ____

   ____

Favorite son Nicolaus Copernicus is depicted on the Polish thousand złoty banknote of 1982. While overseeing lands owned by the local diocese, Copernicus lived at the castle of Olsztyn in Poland and recorded his observations of the heavens.

▶ EXERCISE 5

Translate into Latin.

1. Because of the law of gravity all heavy things from everywhere fall onto the earth.

 ____

2. The earth is so immense that to many people it wrongly seems not to move (literally, be moved).

 ____

3. The sky, however, is boundless in such a way that it cannot move (literally, be moved) around the earth.

 ____

4. It has been asserted that the earth is turning around (literally, being turned around) with a daily movement so that the days are being changed into nights.

 ____

5. Walk in order to watch all parts of the sky!

 ____

6. Go around the world in order to find this element!

 ____

▶ EXERCISE 6

Change the following adjectives into adverbs, keeping the adverbs in the same degree as the adjective.

Example: potentior, potentius <u>potentius</u>

1. fūnestus, a, um ______________
2. gravissimus, a, um ______________
3. miserrimus, a, um ______________
4. brevis, breve ______________
5. ferōx, ferōcis ______________
6. dissimilior, dissimilius ______________
7. altissimus, a, um ______________

▶ EXERCISE 7

Johannes Kepler (1571–1630), a German mathematician and astronomer, continued the work begun by Copernicus and Galileo. His chief contribution to science was defining the laws of planetary motion. The text below is an adapted excerpt from Kepler's work *Somnium* (*The Dream*), in which he describes a voyage from Iceland to the Moon. This work, both a fantasy and a scientific treatise of lunar astronomy, is considered by many a predecessor of the modern science fiction genre. The voyagers, an astronomy student and his mother, an expert in astrology, who both are transported to the moon by mystical forces, have to face very real problems: overcoming the force of gravity (yet to be defined by Isaac Newton), surviving outside the earth's atmosphere, etc. Inertia is also mentioned in this brief excerpt.

Translate the reading passage into English.

Viātor quī ad lūnam ex terrā proficīscitur, tantam vim patitur et tam celeriter trahitur ut paene occidātur. Propter hanc causam necesse est iter facientibus medicāmina capere ut dormiant. Eōrum quoque corpora plicārī dēbent nē in partēs discindantur. Novum perīculum tunc est ingēns frīgus et respīrātiō difficilis. Nē hoc patiātur, viātor spongiam aquae plēnam ad nārēs positam habēre dēbet. Prīmā parte itineris factā rēs faciliōrēs fīunt. Corpus tunc conglobātur tamquam arānea et per sē ipsum sine vī externā movētur.

____

____

____

____

____

____

____

____

arānea, ae, *f.* – spider, cobweb
conglobō, āre, āvī, ātum – to form into a ball
discindō, ere, discidī, discissum – to tear apart
lūna, ae, *f.* – moon
medicāmen, medicāminis, *n.* – medicine
nāris, nāris, *f.* – nostril
plicō, āre, āvī, ātum – to fold
proficīscor, proficīscī, profectus sum – to set out
respīrātiō, respīrātiōnis, *f.* – breathing
spongia, ae, *f.* – sponge
viātor, viātōris, *m.* – voyager, traveler

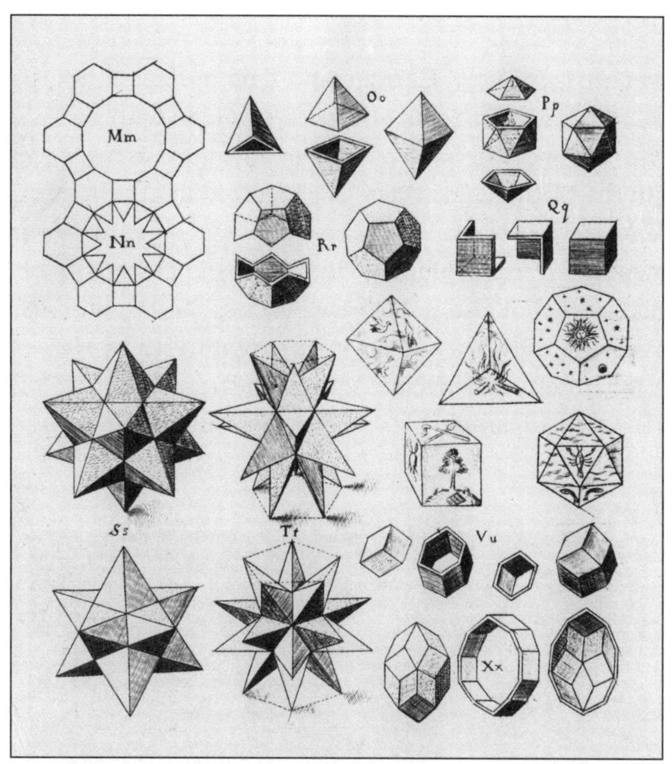

1619 engraving from Kepler's *Harmonia Mundī* which depicts a set of solids that extend the faces of each to form a star, creating the so-called star polyhedra. Two star polyhedra were discovered in 1809 while the others were discovered about two hundred years prior by Kepler.

▶ EXERCISE 8

Using complete Latin sentences, answer the following questions about the reading in Exercise 7.

1. Cūr viātor, quī ex terrā in lūnam proficīscitur, paene occiditur?

   ____

2. Quod remedium (remedy) datur contrā hanc rem?

   ____

3. Quōmodo viātōris corpus pōnī dēbet? Cūr?

   ____

4. Quae aliae rēs sunt in itinere difficilēs?

   ____

5. Quid fierī dēbet ut respīrātiō sit facilior?

   ____

6. Fīuntne rēs difficiliōrēs post prīmam partem itineris? Cūr?

   ____

   ____

▶ EXERCISE 9

Anna Maria van Schurman (1607–1678), of German and Dutch descent, was a friend of the great French philosopher Descartes. Like Erasmus, van Schurman corresponded with many learned women and men of the *rēs pūblica litterārum*, "the republic of literature." While Erasmus also traveled about, van Schurman spent most of her life in Utrecht in the Netherlands where she received many visitors including Queen Christina of Sweden. She was considered the most learned woman of the seventeenth century. Van Schurman received special permission to follow classes, from behind a curtain, at the University of Utrecht. She became proficient not only in Latin and Greek, but also in Hebrew, Arabic, and ten other languages. Van Schurman is celebrated for her writings that logically defended women's right to study. Here is an adapted excerpt of her letter to the medical doctor Johannes Beverovicius "Johan van Beverwijck" (1594–1647), discussing the ruling power that determines the term of human life and the possibilities of human interference.

The portrait of the scholar Anna Maria van Schurman is an engraving by Jonas Suyderhoef (1613–1686) of Haarlem, Netherlands. An eminent engraver of the Dutch Golden Age, Suyderhoef based his work on paintings by the masters. Jan Lievens (1607–1674), who shared a studio with Rembrandt, painted the original portrait.

Translate the passage into English.

Homō frūstrā cōnātur agere contrā ea quae ā Deō sunt dēcrēta. Nihilne igitur valet id quod homō facit? Hoc nōn est vērum. Officium medicōrum est ūtile. Nam medicī rēs faciunt nōn ut voluntātem Deī ēlūdant, sed ut vim morbī frangant, dolōrēs minuant, vīrēs aegrōtī restituant. Hoc fit etiam cum aegrōtus prope mortem versātur. At quamvīs medicus diū et bene aegrōtum cūrāverit, aegrōtus saepe moritur. Tamen dēbēmus officia nostra bene cūrāre, quia ita voluit ille quī nisi optima velle nōn potest.

aegrōtus, a, um – sick, ill
ēlūdō, ere, ēlūsī, ēlūsum – to delude, cheat
frangō, ere, frēgī, fractum – to break
morbus, ī, *m.* – sickness

CONTENT QUESTIONS

After completing Chapter 14, answer these questions.

1. When did Copernicus live? With what discovery is his name mainly associated?

2. What is the title of Copernicus's book said to have laid the foundations of modern astronomy?

3. Which scholar confirmed Copernicus's theories by astronomic observations with a telescope? What was his answer in front of the Inquisition?

4. What is the subject matter of Newton's work *Philosophiae nātūrālis prīncipia mathēmatica* (*Mathematical Principles of Natural Philosophy*) and for what is it famous?

5. What words are usually found in the main clause preceding a result clause?

6. How do we find the supine in *–m* of a verb? What is the main use of this form?

CHAPTER 15

▶ EXERCISE 1

Form the gerund (in all four cases) and the gerundive (only in the nominative singular) of the following verbs.

1. vehō

   ____

   ____

2. appropinquō

   ____

   ____

3. percutiō

   ____

   ____

4. cernō

   ____

   ____

5. rīdeō

   ____

   ____

6. pūniō

   ____

   ____

7. respondeō

   ____

   ____

8. animadvertō

   ____

   ____

▶ EXERCISE 2

Choose the word that is **NOT** derived from the same Latin root.

		a.	b.	c.	d.
1.	_____	a. session	b. siege	c. sedate	d. segment
2.	_____	a. consider	b. reside	c. desire	d. sidereal
3.	_____	a. pugnacious	b. animadversion	c. animosity	d. pusillanimous
4.	_____	a. verse	b. vertebrate	c. veracity	d. adversity
5.	_____	a. approximate	b. proximity	c. propinquity	d. approve
6.	_____	a. discreet	b. cereal	c. secret	d. discern
7.	_____	a. clandestine	b. reclaim	c. proclamation	d. exclamation
8.	_____	a. feign	b. effigy	c. fissure	d. fiction
9.	_____	a. propaganda	b. impinge	c. dispatch	d. pact
10.	_____	a. conflict	b. flicker	c. infliction	d. profligate
11.	_____	a. cussedness	b. rescue	c. repercussion	d. concussion
12.	_____	a. impulse	b. compel	c. peal	d. pelvic
13.	_____	a. deride	b. riding	c. ridicule	d. derisive
14.	_____	a. route	b. corruption	c. rouge	d. abrupt
15.	_____	a. veil	b. invective	c. vehicle	d. inveigh
16.	_____	a. iteration	b. reiterate	c. iterate	d. itinerant
17.	_____	a. circle	b. incinerator	c. research	d. circulation

▶ EXERCISE 3

Translate the following sentences and indicate whether they contain a gerund or a gerundive.

Example: Ars scrībendī mihi placet.
The art of writing pleases me. gerund

1. Spēluncae cōnspiciendae studiōsus in eam dēscendere dēcrēvī.

   ____

2. Amīcīs, quī in terrā exspectābant, dīxeram mē clāmandō ostentūrum esse mē iam dēscendisse.

   ____

   ____

3. In caelum tamen cecidī nec locum dēscendendō invenīre poteram.

   ____

4. Etiam animal ferōx ad mē appropinquāvit, ad quod occīdendum ūsus sum tēlō.

   ____

5. Animālī repellendō ipse repulsus sum ā locō in quō volvēbar et iterum cecidī.

   ____

   ____

6. Cum in novum locum perperam cecidissem, parābar ad fugiendum.

   ____

. . . mē ipsum fūne ligāvī amīcōsque rogāvī ut mē dēmitterent dum mē clāmantem audīrent. (Nicolāī Klimiī iter subterrāneum)

▶ EXERCISE 4

Change the use of *dēbēre* in the following sentences into the passive periphrastic, keeping the tense and mood of the original sentences. Translate the changed sentences.

Example: Patriam amāre dēbēmus.
Patria nōbīs est amanda.
We have/ought to love the fatherland.

1. Aliud animal ferōcissimum ad mē appropinquābat, ex quō fugere dēbēbam.

   ____

   ____

2. Cum (since) arborem proximam cernerem, putāvī mē in eam statim ascendere dēbēre.

   ____

   ____

3. Arbor tamen, quae nōn erat arbor, sed erat mulier, putāvit mē percutī dēbēre.

   ____

   ____

4. Cum oculōs aperuissem, nōn poteram mente fingere quid facere dēbērem.

   ____

   ____

5. Cum animadvertissem undique arborēs circā mē appropinquāre, rīdēre nōn dēbēbam.

   ____

   ____

6. Arborēs tandem dēcrēvērunt mē pūnīrī nōn dēbēre.

   ____

   ____

▶ EXERCISE 5

Translate the following adapted excerpt from Holberg's *Nicolāī Klimiī iter subterrāneum*. The passage discusses the customs of the Potuans, the tree inhabitants of the underground planet which Nicolaus Klim visits.

Est apud Potuānōs optima lēx quae multum facit ad līberōs ēdendōs. Sī quis plūrēs līberōs habet, plūra beneficia quoque accipit et pauciōra eī sunt officia. Sī quis sex habet līberōs, ab omnī pecūniā reī pūblicae dandā līberātur. Hoc est valdē ūtile ad colendās familiās. Nēmō apud Potuānōs plus quam ūnum mūnus habet. Nam omnēs rēs bene sunt faciendae nec potest homō rēs bene facere, sī duōbus labōribus eōdem tempore datur, ut apud nōs fit. Medicī dē ūnō tantum morbō discunt, mūsicī ūnō tantum īnstrūmentō (5) lūdunt. Nam medicus quī cōnātur multōs morbōs cūrāre, nūllum tandem cūrāre valet. Potuānī in nōbilēs et plēbēiōs nōn sēparantur. Intellēxērunt enim hominibus in nōbilēs plēbeiōsque sēparandīs multa odia et bella parārī. Apud eōs omnēs sunt aequī et iūdicantur secundum virtūtem.

____

____

____

____

____

____

____

____

____

____

____

____

____

____

____

____

beneficium, ī, *n.* – benefit
īnstrūmentum, ī, *n.* – instrument
līberī, ōrum, *m. pl.* – children
medicus, ī, *m.* – doctor
morbus, ī, *m.* – illness
mūnus, mūneris, *n.* – job
mūsicus, ī, *m.* – musician
nōbilis, nōbile – noble
plēbēius, a, um – belonging to common people, plebeian
Potuānus, ī, *m.* – Potuan
secundum + *acc.* – according to
sex – six
sī quis – if someone

Posteā intellēxī arborēs illās esse animālia animō menteque praedita, quae quoque ambulāre poterant. (*Nicolāī Klimiī iter subterrāneum*)

▶ EXERCISE 6

Using complete Latin sentences, answer the following questions about the reading in Exercise 5. The Reading Vocabulary of Exercise 5 may be consulted.

1. Quid faciunt Potuānī ad plūrēs līberōs ēdendōs?

   ____

2. Quot (*how many*) līberōs habēre dēbent Potuānī nē ūlla illīs sint officia?

   ____

3. Quot (*how many*) mūnera habēre possunt Potuānī? Cūr?

   ____

4. Quae est secundum Potuānōs magna causa odiī atque bellōrum?

   ____

5. Quid faciunt Potuānī ad odia et bella tollenda?

   ____

6. Videnturne Potuānī fēlīciōrēs quam nōs?

   ____

▶ EXERCISE 7

Complete the following sentences changing the words in parentheses into either a gerund or a gerundive construction. The preposition *ad* may need to be added with the accusative of the gerund or the gerundive. Translate the sentences. The Reading Vocabulary in Exercise 5 may be consulted.

1. Potuānī sunt studiōsī ______________________. (magnam familiam habēre)
   ____

2. ______________________ homō dēbet plūrēs līberōs ēdere. (accipere beneficia)
   ____

3. Nescīmus fueritne lībertās ______________________ Potuānōrum magna. (dēcernere)
   ____

4. ______________________ Potuānī melius prōgrediuntur quam nōs. (omnēs rēs bene facere)
   ____

5. Potuānī in vītā suā parātī sunt ______________________. (ūnum tantum mūnus colere)
   ____

6. ______________________ Potuānī nōbilēs ā plēbēīs nōn sēparant. (odia exstinguere et bella repellere)
   ____

CONTENT QUESTIONS

After completing Chapter 15, answer these questions.

1. Who is the author of *Nicolāī Klimiī iter subterrāneum* and when did he live?
   ____

2. For what primary reason is *Nicolāī Klimiī iter subterrāneum* famous in the history of Latin literature?
   ____

3. With which other works can *Nicolāī Klimiī iter subterrāneum* be compared?
   ____

4. What is the gerund in Latin?
   ____
   ____

5. What is the gerundive in Latin?
   ____
   ____

6. When is the gerundive construction used instead of the gerund?
   ____

7. What is the difference between the ablative and the dative of agent?
   ____
   ____

ENGLISH TO LATIN GLOSSARY

This glossary contains the English meanings of all the Latin words in the **Vocabulary to Learn** sections from all the chapters.

LIST OF ABBREVIATIONS:

(1) = first conjugation
abl. = ablative
acc. = accusative
adj. = adjective
adv. = adverb
conj. = conjunction
dat. = dative
f. = feminine
gen. = genitive
inf. = infinitive
m. = masculine
n. = neuter
pl. = plural
prep. = preposition
sg. = singular

NOTE:

The genitive of second declension words ending in ***–ius*** or ***–ium*** is indicated with a single ***–ī,*** which is the genitive ending itself. Note that in the full form of the genitive there is normally a double ***–i***: *fīlius, –ī* (= *fīliī*); *gaudium, –ī* (= *gaudiī*).

A

abandon, relinquō, -ere, relīquī, relictum
able, to be, possum, posse, potuī, —
able, to be (= *to have the power to do*), valeō, -ēre, valuī, —, + *inf.*
abode, sēdēs, -is, *f.*
abound with, abundō (1), + *abl.*
about, dē, *prep.* + *abl.*
about to be, futūrus, -a, -um, *participle*
absent, absēns, absentis, *adj.*
absent, to be, absum, abesse, āfuī, —
accept, accipiō, -ere, -cēpī, -ceptum
account of, on, propter, *prep.* + *acc.*
account, to hold of no, aestimō ūnīus assis
accuse someone of something, accūsō (1), + *acc.* + *gen.*
accustomed, to be, soleō, -ēre, solitus sum, —, + *inf.*
achieve, nītor, nītī, nīsus/nīxus sum
acknowledge, cognōscō, -ere, cognōvī, cognitum
acquire, cōnsequor, cōnsequī, cōnsecūtus sum; percipiō, -ere, percēpī, perceptum
activity to which one is devoted, studium, -ī, *n.*
add, addō, -ere, addidī, additum
added, to be, accēdō, -ere, accessī, accessum
adopt, capiō, -ere, cēpī, captum
adorned, ōrnātus, -a, -um, *adj.*
advice, cōnsilium, -ī, *n.*
afflict, afflīgō, -ere, afflīxī, afflīctum
after, cum, *conj.* + *pluperfect subjunctive*
after, post, *prep.* + *acc.*
afterward, posteā, *adv.*
again, iterum, *adv.*
against, contrā, *prep.* + *acc.*
age, aetās, -ātis, *f.*
agreeable, iūcundus, -a, -um, *adj.*
agreeableness, grātia, -ae, *f.*
all, omnis, -e, *adj.*
allow somebody to do something, sinō, -ere, sīvī, situm, + *acc.* + *inf.*
allowed for someone to do something, it is, licet, + *dat.* + *inf.*
ally, socius, -ī, *m.*
almost, paene, *adv.*
alone, sōlus, -a, -um, *adj.*
already, iam, *adv.*
also, etiam, *adv.*; quoque, *adv.*
although, cum, *conj.*, + *imperfect subjunctive;* etsī, *conj.;* quamquam, *conj.;* quamvīs, *conj.*
always, semper, *adv.*
ambassador, lēgātus, -ī, *m.*
among, inter, *prep.* + *acc.* (also one of the meanings of *apud*, prep. + acc.)
ancient, antīquus, -a, -um, *adj.*
and, et, *conj.*; atque, *conj.*; -que, *conj.*
and not, nec, *conj.;* neque, *conj.*
and so, itaque, *conj.*
anger, īra, -ae, *f.*
angry, to be, īrāscor, īrāscī, īrātus sum
animal, animal, -ālis, *n.*
another, alius, alia, aliud, *adj.*
answer, respondeō, -ēre, -spondī, -spōnsum
antiquity, antīquitās, -ātis, *f.*
any, ūllus, -a, -um, *indefinite adj. (mainly in negative sentences);* quisquam, quicquam (quidquam), *pronoun*
appear, appāreō, -ēre, appāruī, —
appearance, fōrma, -ae, *f.*
apply, adhibeō, -ēre, adhibuī, adhibitum
appreciative, grātus, -a, -um, *adj.*
approach, accēdō, -ere, accessī, accessum; appropinquō (1)

appropriate, aptus, -a, -um, *adj.*
approve, probō (1)
argument, argūmentum, -ī, *n.*
armed, armātus, -a, -um, *adj.*
army, exercitus, -ūs, *m.*
around, circā, *prep.* + *acc.*; circum, *prep.* + *acc.*
arrival, adventus, -ūs, *m.*
arrive, perveniō, -īre, -vēnī, -ventum
art, ars, artis, *f.*
artisan, artifex, -ficis, *m.*
as, tamquam, *adv.*; ut, *conj.* + *indicative*; atque (*when linked with some form of* īdem)
as . . . as possible, quam + *superlative degree*
as often as, quotiēs, *conj.*
as soon as, simul ac, *conj.*; ut, *conj.* + *perfect indicative*
ash, cinis, -eris, *m.*
ask, ōrō (1); rogō (1)
assert, affirmō (1)
assiduous, frequēns, -entis, *adj.*
associate, socius, -ī, *m.*
at first, prīmō, *adv.*
at home, domī
at last, tandem, *adv.*
at one time . . . at another . . ., modo . . . modo . . .
at the house of, apud, *prep.* + *acc.*
at the same time, simul, *adv.*
athlete, āthlēta, -ae, *m.*
attack, impetus, -ūs, *m.*
attain, cōnsequor, cōnsequī, cōnsecūtus sum
attentiveness, dīligentia, -ae, *f.*
attire, vestis, -is, *f.*
avail, to no, frūstrā, *adv.*
await, exspectō (1)
awaken, excitō (1)
away, absēns, absentis, *adj.*
axis, axis, -is, *m.*
axle, axis, -is, *m.*

B

bad, improbus, -a, -um, *adj.*; malus, -a, -um, *adj.*
baggage, sarcina, -ae, *f.* (used mostly in pl.)
battle, proelium, -ī, *n.*
be, sum, esse, fuī, —
be agreeable to somebody, placeō, -ēre, placuī, placitum, + *dat.*
be away, absum, abesse, āfuī, —
be found, appāreō, -ēre, appāruī
be insane, furō, -ere, furuī, —
be surprised at, mīror, mīrārī, mīrātus sum
be unwilling, nōlō, nōlle, nōluī, —
bear, ferō, ferre, tulī, lātum
beard, barba, -ae, *f.*
beautiful, pulcher, pulchra, pulchrum, *adj.*
because, namque, *conj.*; quia, *conj.*; quod, *conj.*
because of, propter, *prep.* + *acc.*
become, fīō, fierī, factus sum
befall, accidō, -ere, accidī, —
before, in front of, ante, *prep.* + *acc.*
begin to, coepī, coepisse, coeptum, + *inf.*
beginning, initium, -ī, *n.*; ortus, -ūs, *m.*
behalf of, on, prō, *prep.* + *abl.*
behave, act in a certain way, agō, -ere, ēgī, āctum
believe somebody, crēdō, -ere, crēdidī, crēditum, + *dat.*
besides, praeter, *prep.* + *acc.*
best, optimus, -a, -um, *adj.*
bestow, tribuō, -ere, tribuī, tribūtum
better, melior, melius, *adj. comparative*
between, inter, *prep.* + *acc.*
blame, reprehendō, -ere, -prehendī, -prehēnsum
blood, sanguis, -inis, *m.*
blossom, flōreō, -ēre, flōruī, —
body, corpus, -oris, *n.*
bond, necessitūdō, -ūdinis, *f.*
book, liber, librī, *m.*; volūmen, -ūminis, *n.*
born, to be, nāscor, nāscī, nātus sum
born of, to be, orior, orīrī, ortus sum, + *abl.*
bosom, gremium, -ī, *n.*
both . . . and . . ., et . . . et . . .
boundless, īnfīnītus, -a, -um, *adj.*
boy, puer, puerī, *m.*
brave, fortis, -e, *adj.*
break, rumpō, -ere, rūpī, ruptum
bridge, pōns, pontis, *m.*
briefly, breviter, *adv.*
bring about, efficiō, -ere, -fēcī, -fectum, often + *ut*
brook, rīvus, -ī, *m.*
brother, frāter, frātris, *m.*
build, aedificō (1)
building, aedificium, -ī, *n.*
burden, onus, oneris, *n.*; sarcina, -ae, *f.* (used mostly in pl.)
burn, be on fire, ārdeō, -ēre, ārsī, —
burst in, invādō, -ere, invāsī, —
bust, imāgō, imāginis, *f.*
but, at, *conj.*; sed, *conj.*
but that, quīn, *conj.* + *subjunctive*
buy, emō, -ere, ēmī, emptum
by, ā *or* ab, *prep.* + *abl.*

C

calamity, calamitās, -ātis, *f.*
call, vocō (1)
calm, placidus, -a, -um, *adj.*; serēnus, -a, -um, *adj.*
calmly (*of a person's attitude*), aequō animō
camp, castra, -ōrum, *n. pl.*
can, possum, posse, potuī, —
capture, capiō, -ere, cēpī, captum
care, cultus, -ūs, *m.*; cūra, -ae, *f.*
care for, cūrō (1)
care for, not to, aestimō ūnīus assis
careful in choosing, ēlegāns, -antis, *adj.*
carefully, dīligenter, *adv.*
carefulness, dīligentia, -ae, *f.*
carry, ferō, ferre, tulī, lātum; gerō, -ere, gessī, gestum; (*of vehicles*) vehō, -ere, vēxī, vectum
carry back, referō, referre, rettulī, relātum
catch a glimpse of, aspiciō, -ere, aspexī, aspectum
cause, causa, -ae, *f.*
cause to happen, efficiō, -ere, -fēcī, -fectum, often + *ut*
cave, spēlunca, -ae, *f.*
certain, a, quīdam, quaedam, quiddam, *indefinite pronoun*; quīdam, quaedam, quoddam, *indefinite adjective*
certain, for, prō certō, *adverbial phrase*

chain, vinculum, -ī, *n.*

change, mūtō (1)

charm, suāvitās, -ātis, *f.*

chest, pectus, -oris, *n.*

choose, legō, -ere, lēgī, lēctum

circle, orbis, orbis, *m.*

citizen, cīvis, -is, *m./f.*

city (city of Rome), urbs, urbis, *f.*

clear, clārus, -a, -um, *adj.*; serēnus, -a, -um, *adj.*

clear, to be, appāreō, -ēre, appāruī, —

close friend, familiāris, -is, *m./f.*

closest, intimus, -a, -um, *adj.*

clothes, vestīmenta, -ōrum, *n. pl.*; vestis, -is, *f.*

cloud, nūbēs, -is, *f.*

cold, frīgus, -oris, *n.*

column of marching or traveling people, agmen, -minis, *n.*

combat, proelium, -ī, *n.*

come, veniō, -īre, vēnī, ventum

come upon, inveniō, -īre, invēnī, inventum

command, potestās, -ātis, *f.*

commanding officer, imperātor, -ōris, *m.*

common, pūblicus, -a, -um, *adj.*

common people, vulgus, -ī, *n.*

commonplace, mediocris, -e, *adj.*

compel, cōgō, -ere, coēgī, coactum

complete, to, compleō, -ēre, -ēvī, -ētum

concerning, dē, *prep.* + *abl.*

condition, condiciō, -ōnis, *f.*

confirm, sanciō, -īre, sānxī, sanctum

conflagration, incendium, -ī, *n.*

confusion, tumultus, -ūs, *m.*

connect, coniungō, -ere, -iūnxī, -iūnctum

connection (*usually by marriage*), affīnitās, -ātis, *f.*

conquer, vincō, -ere, vīcī, victum

consider, arbitror, arbitrārī, arbitrātus sum; putō (1)

consist in, cōnstō, -āre, cōnstitī, —, + *abl.*

constancy, cōnstantia, -ae, *f.*

constellation, sīdus, -eris, *n.*

consul, cōnsul, -ulis, *m.*

consult, cōnsulō, -ere, cōnsuluī, cōnsultum, + *acc.*

consume, cōnsūmō, -ere, -sūmpsī, -sūmptum

contain, contineō, -ēre, continuī, contentum

contempt, to regard with, contemnō, -ere, contempsī, contemptum

control, potestās, -ātis, *f.*

cook, coquō, -ere, coxī, coctum

cottage, casa, -ae, *f.*

count among, numerō (1)

country house, vīlla, -ae, *f.*

countryside, rūs, rūris, *n.*

courage, fortitūdō, -inis, *f.*; virtūs, -ūtis, *f.*

cover, tegō, -ere, tēxī, tēctum

craftsman, artifex, -ficis, *m.*

crowd, multitūdō, -ūdinis, *f.*

crowded, celeber, -bris, -bre, *adj.*

cruel, crūdēlis, -e, *adj.*

cry, fleō, -ēre, flēvī, flētum

cultivate, colō, -ere, coluī, cultum

cultured, litterātus, -a, -um, *adj.*

custom, cōnsuētūdō, -ūdinis, *f.*; mōs, mōris, *m.*

D

daily, cottīdiānus, -a, -um, *adj.*

danger, perīculum, -ī, *n.*

darkness, tenebrae, -ārum, *f. pl.*

daughter, fīlia, -ae, *f.*

day, diēs, -ēī, *m./f.*

deadly, fūnestus, -a, -um, *adj.*

dear, cārus, -a, -um, *adj.*

death, mors, mortis, *f.*

deceive, dēcipiō, -ere, dēcēpī, dēceptum

deception, dolus, -ī, *m.*

decide, dēcernō, -ere, -crēvī, -crētum, + *inf.*

deeds, rēs gestae

deep, altus, -a, -um, *adj.*

defeat, vincō, -ere, vīcī, victum

defend, dēfendō, -ere, dēfendī, dēfēnsum

dejected, to become, animum dēmittō

delight, dēliciae, -ārum, *f. pl.* (*noun*)

delight, dēlectō (1) (*verb*)

delightful, iūcundus, -a, -um, *adj.*

demonstrate, dēclārō (1)

deny, negō (1)

descend, dēscendō, -ere, -scendī, -scēnsum

descended from, to be, orior, orīrī, ortus sum, + *abl.*

design, parō (1)

desire, cupiō, -ere, -īvī, -ītum; dēsīderō (1)

despise, contemnō, -ere, contempsī, contemptum

destiny, fātum, -ī, *n.*

destroy, dēleō, -ēre, dēlēvī, dēlētum; tollō, -ere, sustulī, sublātum

determine, dēcernō, -ere, -crēvī, -crētum, + *inf.*

devastate, dēvastō (1)

devoid of, expers, -ertis, *adj.* + *gen.*

die, dēcēdō, -ere, dēcessī, dēcessum; morior, morī, mortuus sum

difficult, difficilis, -e, *adj.*

diligence, dīligentia, -ae, *f.*

diligently, dīligenter, *adv.*

dine, cēnō (1)

dinner party, convīvium, -ī, *n.*

direct, moderor, -ārī, -ātus sum

disadvantage, incommodum, -ī, *n.*

disaster, calamitās, -ātis, *f.*; clādēs, -is, *f.*

disgraceful, turpis, -e, *adj.*

dispute, līs, lītis, *f.*

dissimilar, dissimilis, -e, *adj.*

distinguish by the eyes, cernō, -ere, crēvī, crētum

distinguished, clārus, -a, -um, *adj.*; illūstris, -e, *adj.*; praeclārus, -a, -um, *adj.*

distress, afflīgō, -ere, afflīxī, afflīctum

distribute, partior, partīrī, partītus sum

divide, partior, partīrī, partītus sum

divine, dīvīnus, -a, -um, *adj.*

do, agō, -ere, ēgī, āctum; faciō, -ere, fēcī, factum

dominate, dominor, dominārī, dominātus sum

down from, dē, *prep.* + *abl.*

drag, trahō, -ere, traxī, tractum

draw, trahō, -ere, trāxī, trāctum

drink, bibō, -ere, bibī, —

drive, agō, -ere, ēgī, āctum; vehō, -ere, vēxī, vectum

drive into, impingō, -ere, impēgī, impāctum
duty, officium, -ī, *n.*
dwell, habitō (1)
dwelling, aedēs, -ium, *f. pl.*

E

each, omnis, -e, *adj.*
eager for, to be, studeō, -ēre, studuī, —, + *dat.*
ear, auris, -is, *f.*
earn, percipiō, -ere, percēpī, perceptum
earth, orbis terrārum
east, ortus sōlis
easy, facilis, -e, *adj.*
eat, comedō, -ere, -ēdī, -ēsum
effect, to (to bring about), efficiō, -ere, -fēcī, -fectum, often + *ut*
either . . . or . . ., aut . . . aut . . .
elaborate, ōrnātus, -a, -um, *adj.*
element, elementum, -ī, *n.*
emperor, Caesar, -aris, *m.* (initially the name of Julius Caesar); imperātor, -ōris, *m.*
empire, imperium, -ī, *n.*
empty of, vacuus, -a, -um, + *abl.*
end, fīnis, -is, *m.*
endless, immēnsus, -a, -um, *adj.*
endowed with, praeditus, -a, -um, + *abl.*
endure, patior, patī, passus sum
enemy, hostis, -is, *m.*; inimīcus, -ī, *m.*
enjoy, fruor, fruī, fruitus/frūctus sum, + *abl.*
enjoy the society of, fruor, fruī, fruitus /frūctus sum, + *abl.*
enough, satis, *adv.*
enter, intrō (1)
entire, tōtus, -a, -um, *adj.*
entreat, ōrō (1)
envy someone, invideō, -ēre, invīdī, invīsum, + *dat.*
equal, pār, paris, *adj.*
eruption, incendium, -ī, *n.*
especially, praecipuē, *adv.*; praesertim, *adv.*
establish, cōnstituō, -ere, cōnstituī, cōnstitūtum
esteem, exīstimō (1)
esteem a lot, magnī habeō
esteem highly, dīligō, -ere, dīlēxī, dīlēctum
estimate, aestimō (1); exīstimō (1)
even, aequus, -a, -um, *adj.*
even, etiam, *adv.*
ever, umquam, *adv.*
every, omnis, -e, *adj.*
everywhere, ubīque, *adv.*
example, exemplar, -āris, *n.*; exemplum, -ī, *n.*
exceedingly, valdē, *adv.*
except, praeter, *prep.* + *acc.*
exclaim, exclāmō (1)
exhort, hortor, hortārī, hortātus sum
expect, exspectō (1)
expense, sumptus, -ūs, *m.*
exploits, rēs gestae
extent, to a small, paulō, *adv.*
extent, to such an, adeō, *adv.*
extent, to what, quantum, *interrogative and relative adv.*
external, externus, -a, -um, *adj.*
extinguish, exstinguō, -ere, -stīnxī, -stīnctum
eye, oculus, -ī, *m.*

F

face, faciēs, -ēī, *f.*; vultus, -ūs, *m.*
faith, fidēs, -eī, *f.*
faithful, fidēlis, -e, *adj.*
fall, cadō, -ere, cecidī, cāsum
fall upon, accidō, -ere, accidī, —
fame, fāma, -ae, *f.*
familiarity, familiāritās, -ātis, *f.*
family member, familiāris, -āris, *m./f.*
family, familia, -ae, *f.*
famous, praeclārus, -a, -um, *adj.*
far, longē, *adv.*; procul, *adv.*
far away, procul, *adv.*
farmer, agricola, -ae, *m.*
fate, fātum, -ī, *n.*; sors, sortis, *f.* (*in the metaphorical sense of one's condition in life*)
father, pater, patris, *m.*
fatherland, patria, -ae, *f.*
favor, beneficium, -ī, *n.*; grātia, -ae, *f.*; officium, -ī, *n.*
fear, timor, -ōris, *m.* (*noun*)
fear, timeō, -ēre, timuī, —; vereor, -ērī, veritus sum (*verb*)
feast, convīvium, -ī, *n.*
feed, alō, -ere, aluī, altum/alitum
feel, sentiō, -īre, sēnsī, sēnsum
ferocious, ferōx, -ōcis, *adj.*
fetter, vinculum, -ī, *n.*
fever, febris, -is, *f.*
few, paucī, -ae, -a, *adj.*
field, ager, agrī, *m.*
fierce, ācer, ācris, ācre, *adj.*; ferōx, -ōcis, *adj.*
fight, pugnō (1)
fill, compleō, -ēre, -ēvī, -ētum
finally, tandem, *adv.*
find, inveniō, -īre, invēnī, inventum
find to be, cognōscō, -ere, cognōvī, cognitum
finger, digitus, -ī, *m.*
fire, ignis, -is, *m.*
first, prīmum, *adv.*; **at first,** prīmō, *adv.*
first, prīmus, -a, -um, *adj.*
fish, piscis, -is, *m.*
fitted, aptus, -a, -um, *adj.*
flame, flamma, -ae, *f.*
flee, fugiō, -ere, fūgī, —
fleet, classis, -is, *f.*
flesh, carō, carnis, *f.*
flourish, flōreō, -ēre, flōruī, —
flow, fluō, -ere, flūxī, fluxum
follow, sequor, sequī, secūtus sum
fond of, studiōsus, -a, -um, *adj.* + *gen.*
food, cibus, -ī, *m.*
for, enim, *conj.*; nam, *conj.*; namque, *conj.*
for, prō, *prep.* + *abl.*
force, impetus, -ūs, *m.*; vīs, —, *f.*, *pl.* vīrēs, vīrium (*noun*)
force, cōgō, -ere, coēgī, coactum (*verb*)
foreign to, aliēnus, -a, -um, *adj.* + *prep. ā/ab* + *abl.*
forest, silva, -ae, *f.*
forget, oblīvīscor, oblīvīscī, oblītus sum, + *gen.*
forgetful of, immemor, -oris, *adj.* + *gen.*
forgiveness, venia, -ae, *f.*
form, fōrma, -ae, *f.*
form in the mind, fingō, -ere, fīnxī, fictum

fortunate, fēlīx, -īcis, *adj.*; prosper, prospera, prosperum, *adj.*

fortune, fortūna, -ae, *f.*

Fortune, the goddess, Fortūna, -ae, *f.*

Forum Rōmānum, the main square in Rome, forum, -ī, *n.*

free, līber, lībera, līberum, *adj.*

free someone from something, līberō (1), + *acc.* + *abl.*

free time, ōtium, -ī, *n.*

freedom, lībertās, -ātis, *f.*

frequent, frequēns, -entis, *adj.*

friend, amīcus, -ī, *m.*

friendly, amīcus, -a, -um, *adj.*

from, ā *or* ab, *prep.* + *abl.*; ē *or* ex, *prep.* + *abl.*

from all parts, undique, *adv.*

from all sides, undique, *adv.*

from everywhere, undique, *adv.*

fruit, pōmum, -ī, *n.*

full of, plēnus, -a, -um, *adj.* + *gen.* or + *abl.*

G

gain, lūcrum, -ī, *n.* (*noun*)

gain, cōnsequor, cōnsequī, cōnsecūtus sum (*verb*)

garden, hortus, -ī, *m.*

garment, vestīmentum, -ī, *n.*

garrison, praesidium, -ī, *n.*

gate, porta, -ae, *f.*

gem, gemma, -ae, *f.*

general, dux, ducis, *m.*; imperātor, -ōris, *m.*

generosity, līberālitās, -ātis, *f.*

get, percipiō, -ere, percēpī, perceptum

get ready, parō (1)

get to know, cognōscō, -ere, cognōvī, cognitum

gift, dōnum, -ī, *n.*

girl, puella, -ae, *f.*

girl of marriageable age, virgō, -inis, *f.*

give, dō, dăre, dedī, dătum

give back, reddō, -ere, reddidī, redditum

give birth to, pariō, -ere, peperī, partum; gignō, -ere, genuī, genitum

give forth, ēdō, -ere, ēdidī, ēditum

glide down, lābor, lābī, lāpsus sum

glimpse, aspiciō, -ere, aspexī, aspectum

glory, glōria, -ae, *f.*

go, eō, īre, īvī, itum

go around, circumeō, -īre, -īvī, -itum

go away, dēcēdō, -ere, dēcessī, dēcessum

go back, redeō, -īre, -īvī, -itum

go forward, prōgredior, prōgredī, prōgressus sum

go to, petō, -ere, petīvī, petītum

god, deus, -ī, *m.*

goddess, dea, -ae, *f.*

going to be, futūrus, -a, -um, *participle*

gold, aurum, -ī, *n.*

good, bonus, -a, -um, *adj.*

goodbye!, valē!

good will, benevolentia, -ae, *f.*

grant, tribuō, -ere, tribuī, tribūtum

gravity, gravitās, -ātis, *f.*

great, magnus, -a, -um, *adj.*

greater, maior, maius, *adj. comparative*

greater amount, amplius, *adv.*

greater number, amplius, *adv.*

greatest, maximus, -a, -um, *adj. superlative*

greet, salūtō (1)

greet, I (*a customary way to begin a letter*), salūtem dīcō, + *dat.*

grief, dolor, -ōris, *m.*

grieve, doleō, -ēre, doluī, —

grow, crēscō, -ere, crēvī, —

guard, custōs, -ōdis, *m.*

guide, moderor, moderārī, moderātus sum

H

habit, cōnsuētūdō, -ūdinis, *f.*; mōs, mōris, *m.*

hand, manus, -ūs, *f.*

hang (*intransitive*), pendeō, -ēre, pependī, —

happen, accidō, -ere, accidī, —

happen (*impersonal*), fīō, fierī, factus sum

happen upon, offendō, -ere, offendī, offēnsum

happy, fēlīx, -īcis, *adj.*

hardly, vix, *adv.*

harm, incommodum, -ī, *n.* (*noun*)

harm, laedō, -ere, laesī, laesum (*verb*)

hate someone/something, odiō habēre, + *acc.*

hatred, odium, -ī, *n.*

have, habeō, -ēre, habuī, habitum

having no share in, expers, expertis, *adj.* + *gen.*

he, she, it, is, ea, id, *personal and demonstrative pronoun and adj.*

head, caput, -itis, *n.*

head for, petō, -ere, petīvī, petītum

heal, sānō (1)

health, salūs, -ūtis, *f.*; valētūdō, -ūdinis, *f.*

health, to be in good, valeō, -ēre, valuī, —, + *inf.*

hear, audiō, -īre, audīvī, audītum

heart, cor, cordis, *n.*

heaven, caelum, -ī, *n.*

heavy, gravis, -e, *adj.*

heir, hērēs, -ēdis, *m./f.*

help, auxilium, -ī, *n.* (*noun*)

help, adiuvō, -āre, adiūvī, adiūtum (*verb*)

helplessness, inopia, -ae, *f.*

hence, quārē, *conj.*

her (own), suus, -a, -um, *possessive adj.*

herself, suī, sibi, sē, *reflexive pronoun*

hide, skin, pellis, -is, *f.* (*noun*)

hide, occultō (1) (*verb*)

highest, summus, -a, -um, *adj.*

hill, collis, -is, *m.*

himself, suī, sibi, sē, *reflexive pronoun*

hold, contineō, -ēre, continuī, contentum; teneō, -ēre, tenuī, tentum

home, domus, -ūs, *f.*

honor, honor, -ōris, *m.*

hope, spēs, speī, *f.* (*noun*)

hope, spērō (1) (*verb*)

horn, cornū, -ūs, *n.*

horse, equus, -ī, *m.*

horseman, eques, -itis, *m.*

house, aedēs, -ium, *f. pl.*; domus, -ūs, *f.*; tēctum, -ī, *n.*

household, familia, -ae, *f.*

how, quam, *interrogative adv. and exclamation particle*; quōmodo, *adv.*

how great, quantus, -a, -um, *interrogative and relative adj.*

how long, quamdiū, *interrogative and relative adv.*

how much, quantus, -a, -um, *interrogative and relative adj.*

however, autem, *conj.*; tamen, *conj.*

huge, ingēns, ingentis, *adj.*

human, hūmānus, -a, -um, *adj.*

human character, hūmānitās, -ātis, *f.*

humanity, hūmānitās, -ātis, *f.*

humble, humilis, -e, *adj.*

hurt (*i.e., feel pain - intransitive*), doleō, -ēre, doluī, —

husband, marītus, -ī, *m.*

I

I, ego, *personal pronoun*

ice, glaciēs, -ēī, *f.*

if, sī, *conj.*

if not, nisi, *conj.*

if only (*a particle of wishing*), utinam

illness, morbus, -ī, *m.*

illustrious, illūstris, -e, *adj.*

image, imāgō, -inis, *f.*

imagine, fingō, -ere, finxī, fictum

immeasurable, immēnsus, -a, -um, *adj.*

immediately, statim, *adv.*

immense, immēnsus, -a, -um, *adj.*

immortal, immortālis, -e, *adj.*

impede, impediō, -īre, -īvī, -ītum

impetus, impetus, -ūs, *m.*

important, magnus, -a, -um, *adj.*

in, in, *prep.* + *abl.*

in fact, enim, *conj.*; nam, *conj.*

in Latin, Latīnē, *adv.*

in order not to, nē, *conj.* + *subjunctive*

in order to, ut + *subjunctive*

in such a way, sīc, *adv.*

in the morning, māne, *adv.*

in vain, frūstrā, *adv.*

inconsistent with, aliēnus, -a, -um, *adj.* + *prep.* *ā/ab* + *abl.*

incorrectly, perperam, *adv.*

increase, augeō, -ēre, auxī, auctum

indeed, namque, *conj.*; quidem, *adv.*

indication, argūmentum, -ī, *n.*

indifferently, aequō animō, *adverbial phrase*

indulgence, venia, -ae, *f.*

inert, to be, iaceō, -ēre, iacuī, —

inflict, īnflīgō, -ere, īnflīxī, īnflīctum

inhabitant, incola, -ae, *m.*

inheritance, hērēditās, -ātis, *f.*

injury, iniūria, -ae, *f.*

injustice, inīquitās, -ātis, *f.*

innermost, intimus, -a, -um, *adj.*

interested in, to be, studeō, -ēre, studuī, —, + *dat.*

into, ad, *prep.* + *acc.*; in, *prep.* + *acc.*

invade, to, invādō, -ere, invāsī, —

island, īnsula, -ae, *f.*

it, she, he, is, ea, id, *personal and demonstrative pronoun and adj.*

Italy, Italia, -ae, *f.*

itself, suī, sibi, sē, *reflexive pronoun*

J

javelin, tēlum, -ī, *n.*

join, iungō, -ere, iūnxī, iūnctum

join together, coniungō, -ere, -iūnxī, -iūnctum

joke, iocus, -ī, *m.*

joy, gaudium, -ī, *n.*

judge, iūdex, -icis, *m.* (*noun*)

judge, arbitror, -ārī, -ātus sum; iūdicō (1) (*verb*)

just, iūstus, -a, -um, *adj.*

just as, sīcut, *adv.*

K

keen, ācer, ācris, ācre, *adj.*

keep quiet, taceō, -ēre, tacuī, tacitum

keep silent, taceō, -ēre, tacuī, tacitum

keep together, contineō, -ēre, continuī, contentum

kill, occīdō, -ere, occīdī, occīsum

kind, genus, -eris, *n.*

kindness, beneficium, -ī, *n.*; hūmānitās, -ātis, *f.*

king, rēx, rēgis, *m.*

knight, member of the equestrian order, eques, -itis, *m.*

know, sciō, -īre, -īvī, -ītum; to know (a person) *cognōvī* (perfect tense of *cognōscō*)

know, not to, nesciō, -īre, -īvī, -ītum

L

labor, labor, -ōris, *m.*

lack something, to, egeō, -ēre, eguī, —, + *abl.*; indigeō, -ēre, indiguī, —, + *abl.*

lacking in, expers, -ertis, *adj.* + *gen.*

land, terra, -ae, *f.*

language, lingua, -ae, *f.*

lap, gremium, -ī, *n.*

large, magnus, -a, -um, *adj.*

last, extrēmus, -a, -um, *adj.*

Latin, Latīnus, -a, -um, *adj.*; **in Latin,** Latīnē, *adv.*

laugh, rīdeō, -ēre, rīsī, rīsum

law, lēx, lēgis, *f.*

lead, agō, -ere, ēgī, āctum; dūcō, -ere, dūxī, ductum

leader, dux, ducis, *m.*

leading citizen, prīnceps, prīncipis, *m.*

learn, discō, -ere, didicī, —

learned, doctus, -a, -um, *adj.*

least, minimē, *adv. superlative*

leave, discēdō, -ere, -cessī, -cessum

leave behind, relinquō, -ere, relīquī, relictum

leave over, reliquum facere

legitimate, iūstus, -a, -um, *adj.*

leisure, ōtium, -ī, *n.*

less, minus, *adv. comparative*

lest, nē, *conj.* + *subjunctive*

let my spirit sink, to, animum dēmittō

letter (epistle), epistula, -ae, *f.*; litterae, -ārum, *f. pl.*

letter of the alphabet, littera, -ae, *f.*

lie, mendācium, -ī, *n.*

lie down, iaceō, -ēre, iacuī, —

life, vīta, -ae, *f.*

lift up, tollō, -ere, sustulī, sublātum

light, levis, -e, *adj.*

light, lūmen, -inis, *n.* (*noun*)

like, similis, -e, *adj.* + *gen.* or + *dat.*

line of verse, versus, -ūs, *m.*

line of writing, versus, -ūs, *m.*

listen, audiō, -īre, audīvī, audītum

literate, litterātus, -a, -um, *adj.*

literature, litterae, -ārum, *f. pl.*

little house, casa, -ae, *f.*

little, somewhat, paulō, *adv.*

live, habitō (1); vīvō, -ere, vīxī, vīctum

located, situs, -a, -um, *adj.*

long, longus, -a, -um, *adj.*

long for, dēsīderō (1)

long time, for a, diū, *adv.*

look after, cōnsulō, -ere, cōnsuluī, cōnsultum, + *dat.*

look at, aspiciō, -ere, aspexī, aspectum; cōnspiciō, -ere, -spexī, -spectum; tueor, -ērī, tuitus/tūtus sum

look for, quaerō, -ere, quaesīvī, quaesītum

look here!, ecce, *interj.*

lord, dominus, -ī, *m.*

lose, āmittō, -ere, -mīsī, -missum; perdō, -ere, perdidī, perditum

lot, sors, sortis, *f.* (*in the literal sense of a lot one draws*), fate (*in the metaphorical sense of one's condition in life*)

love, amor, -ōris, *m.* (*noun*)

love, amō (1); dīligō, -ere, dīlēxī, dīlēctum (*verb*)

low, humilis, -e, *adj.*

loyal, fidēlis, -e, *adj.*

M

made, to be, fīō, fierī, factus sum

made of wood, ligneus, -a, -um, *adj.*

magistracy, magistrātus, -ūs, *m.*

magistrate, magistrātus, -ūs, *m.*

maintain, affirmō (1)

make, faciō, -ere, fēcī, factum

make available, praestō, -āre, praestitī, praestitum

make known, dēclārō (1)

man (*i.e., human being*), homō, -inis, *m.*

man, vir, virī, *m.*

manage, moderor, moderārī, moderātus sum

management, cultus, -ūs, *m.*

manner, modus, -ī, *m.*

many, multus, -a, -um, *adj.*

marching column, agmen, agminis, *n.*

maritime, maritimus, -a, -um, *adj.*

marriage, mātrimōnium, -ī, *n.*; nūptiae, -ārum, *f. pl.*

marry (*a woman*), uxōrem dūcō

marvel, mīror, mīrārī, mīrātus sum

master, dominus, -ī, *m.*

matter, rēs, reī, *f.*

meat, carō, carnis, *f.*

mediocre, mediocris, -e, *adj.*

meet, conveniō, -īre, -vēnī, -ventum

member of the equestrian order, eques, -itis, *m.*

memory, memoria, -ae, *f.*

method, modus, -ī, *m.*

midday, merīdiēs, -ēī, *m.*

middle, medius, -a, -um, *adj.*

middle, the, medium, -ī, *n.*

middling, mediocris, -e, *adj.*

midst, medium, -ī, *n.*

might, with all one's, prō vīribus

military escort, praesidium, -ī, *n.*

mind, animus, -ī, *m.*; mēns, mentis, *f.*; opīniō, opīniōnis, *f.*

mindful of (*usually of one's obligations*), memor, -oris, *adj.* + *gen.*

misfortune, calamitās, -ātis, *f.*

mistake, to make a, errō (1)

mistress, domina, -ae, *f.*

moderate, mediocris, -e, *adj.*

money, pecūnia, -ae, *f.*

morals, mōrēs, -um, *m. pl.*

more (*in amount*), amplius, *adv.*; magis, *adv.*

more (*in number*), plūrēs, plūra, *adj. comparative*

more, plūs, plūris, *adj. comparative*

morning, in the, māne, *adv.*

most, maximē, *adv. superlative*

most, plūrimus, -a, -um, *adj. superlative*

most intimate, intimus, -a, -um, *adj.*

mother, māter, mātris, *f.*

motion, mōtus, -ūs, *m.*

mountain, mōns, montis, *m.*

mouth, ōs, ōris, *n.*

move, moveō, -ēre, mōvī, mōtum

movement, mōtus, -ūs, *m.*

much, multum, *adv.*; **by much,** multō, *adv.*

much, multus, -a, -um, *adj.*

must, dēbeō, -ēre, dēbuī, dēbitum, + *inf.*

my, meus, -a, -um, *possessive adj.*

N

name, nōmen, -inis, *n.*; fāma, -ae, *f.*

nature, nātūra, -ae, *f.*

near, prope, *prep.* + *acc.*

nearest, proximus, -a, -um, *adj.*

necessarily, necessāriō, *adv.*

necessary, necessārius, -a, -um, *adj.*

necessary for someone to do something, it is, necesse est, + *dat.* + *inf.*

need, dēsīderō (1); indigeō, -ēre, indiguī, —, + *abl.*

neglect, neglegō, -ere, neglēxī, neglēctum

neither, neuter, neutra, neutrum, *adj.*

neither . . . nor . . ., nec . . . nec . . .; neque . . . neque . . .

never, numquam, *adv.*

nevertheless, tamen, *adv.*

new, novus, -a, -um, *adj.*

nice, pulcher, pulchra, pulchrum, *adj.*; iūcundus, -a, -um, *adj.*

night, nox, noctis, *f.*; **by night, at night,** noctū, *adv.*

no, not at all, minimē, *adv. superlative*

no one, nēmō, *m.*

none, nūllus, -a, -um, *adj.*

none (of two), neuter, neutra, neutrum, *adj.*

nor, nec, *conj.*

northern, septentriōnālis, -e, *adj.*

not, nōn, *negative adv.*

not even, nē . . . quidem . . .

not only . . ., but also . . ., nōn sōlum . . ., sed etiam . . .

not to, nē, *conj.*

not to know, nesciō, -īre, -īvī, -ītum

not to want, nōlō, nōlle, nōluī, —

nothing, nihil, *negative pronoun*

notice, animadvertō, -ere, animadvertī, animadversum

nourish, alō, -ere, aluī, altum/alitum

now, nunc, *adv.*

now . . . now . . ., modo . . . modo . . .

nowhere, nusquam, *adv.*

number, numerus, -ī, *m.* (*noun*)

number, numerō (1) (*verb*)

O

observe, cōnspiciō, -ere, -spexī, -spectum

obvious, to be, appāreō, -ēre, appāruī, —

occupied in, to be, versor, versārī, versātus sum

occupy, occupō (1)

occur, ūsū venīre

of every day, cottīdiānus, -a, -um, *adj.*

offend, offendō, -ere, offendī, offēnsum

offer, praestō, -āre, praestitī, praestitum

office of a magistrate, magistrātus, -ūs, *m.*

often, saepe, *adv.*

old, vetus, veteris, *adj.;* vetustus, -a, -um, *adj.*

old age, senectūs, -ūtis, *f.*

old man, senex, -is, *m.*

on, in, *prep. + abl.*

on account of, propter, *prep. + acc.*

on behalf of, prō, *prep. + abl.*

once, semel, *adv.*

one, ūnus, ūna, ūnum, *adj.*

one apiece, singulī, -ae, -a, *adj.*

one each (*a distributive*), singulī, -ae, -a, *adj.*

one time . . . at another . . ., modo . . . modo . . .

only, sōlus, -a, -um, *adj.*

only, tantum, *adv.*

open, aperiō, -īre, aperuī, apertum

opinion, opīniō, opīniōnis, *f.;* sententia, -ae, *f.*

opponent, inimīcus, -ī, *m.*

or, aut, *conj.;* vel, *conj.*

oracle, ōrāculum, -ī, *n.*

order, ōrdō, ōrdinis, *m.;* iussus, -ūs, *m.* (*usually employed in the ablative singular only*)

order somebody to do something, iubeō, -ēre, iussī, iussum, + *acc.* + *inf.*

ordinary, mediocris, -e, *adj.*

origin, orīgō, orīginis, *f.;* ortus, -ūs, *m.*

originate, orior, orīrī, ortus sum, + *abl.*

ornate, ōrnātus, -a, -um, *adj.*

other, alius, alia, aliud, *adj.*

other (*of two*), alter, altera, alterum, *adj.*

ought, dēbeō, -ēre, dēbuī, dēbitum, + *inf.*

our, noster, nostra, nostrum, *possessive adj.*

out of, ē *or* ex, *prep. + abl.*

outside, in the open, forīs, *adv.*

outside of, extrā, *prep. + acc.*

outward, externus, -a, -um, *adj.*

overwhelm, opprimō, -ere, oppressī, oppressum

owe, dēbeō, -ēre, dēbuī, dēbitum, + *inf.*

P

pain, dolor, -ōris, *m.*

pain, to feel, doleō, -ēre, doluī, —

painting, imāgō, imāginis, *f.*

pardon, venia, -ae, *f.*

parent, parēns, -rentis, *m./f.*

part, pars, partis, *f.*

particularly, praecipuē, *adv.*

partner, socius, -ī, *m.*

passages of a book, locī, -ōrum, *m. pl.*

past actions, rēs gestae

peace, pāx, pācis, *f.*

peaceful, placidus, -a, -um, *adj.*

people, hominēs, -um, *m. pl.;* populus, -ī, *m.*

perceive (with the eyes), cernō, -ere, crēvī, crētum

perhaps, fortasse, *adv.*

permitted for someone to do something, it is, licet, + *dat.* + *inf.*

pertaining to Latin, Latīnus, -a, -um, *adj.*

pet, dēliciae, -ārum, *f. pl.*

place, locus, -ī, *m.* (*noun*)

place, pōnō, -ere, posuī, positum (*verb*)

places (*geographical*), loca, -ōrum, *n. pl.*

plan, cōnsilium, -ī, *n.;* **make plans,** cōnsilia capere

plant, herba, -ae, *f.*

play, lūdō, -ere, lūsī, lūsum

pleasant, iūcundus, -a, -um, *adj.*

please, dēlectō (1); placeō, -ēre, placuī, placitum, + *dat.*

please (*to be agreeable to*), placeō, -ēre, placuī, placitum, + *dat.*

poem, carmen, -inis, *n.*

poet, poēta, -ae, *m.*

point of view, sententia, -ae, *f.*

poison, venēnum, -ī, *n.*

poor, pauper, pauperis, *adj.*

populace, populus, -ī, *m.*

population, gēns, gentis, *f.*

possess, possideō, -ēre, possēdī, possessum

possessed of, praeditus, -a, -um, + *abl.*

pour, fundō, -ere, fūdī, fūsum

power, imperium, -ī, *n.;* potentia, -ae, *f.;* potestās, -ātis, *f.*

powerful, potēns, potentis, *adj.*

practical intelligence, prūdentia, -ae, *f.*

praise, laudō, -āre, -āvī, -ātum

prayer, prex, precis, *f.*

precious stone, gemma, -ae, *f.*

prefer, mālō, mālle, māluī, —

prepare, parō (1)

preserve, servō (1)

prevent, impediō, -īre, -īvī, -ītum

proceed, prōgredior, prōgredī, prōgressus sum

produce, ēdō, -ere, ēdidī, ēditum; gignō, -ere, genuī, genitum

profit, lūcrum, -ī, *n.*

promise, polliceor, pollicērī, pollicitus sum; prōmittō, -ere, prōmīsī, prōmissum

proof, argūmentum, -ī, *n.*

prosperous, prosper, prospera, prosperum, *adj.*

protect, tegō, -ere, tēxī, tēctum; tueor, -ērī, tuitus/tūtus sum

provide, praestō, -āre, praestitī, praestitum

provided with, praeditus, -a, -um, + *abl.*

public (*belonging to the state*), pūblicus, -a, -um, *adj.*

public office or distinction, honor, -ōris, *m.*

public, the (*i.e., common people*), vulgus, -ī, *n.*

punish, pūniō, -īre, -īvī, -ītum

pursuit, studium, -ī, *n.*

push, impingō, -ere, impēgī, impāctum

push back, repellō, -ere, reppulī, repulsum

put, pōnō, -ere, posuī, positum

Q

quarrel, līs, lītis, *f.*

queen, rēgīna, -ae, *f.*

R

rage, furō, -ere, furuī, —

raise, tollō, -ere, sustulī, sublātum

raising, ortus, -ūs, *m.*

rather, potius, *adv.*

ratify solemnly, sanciō, -īre, sānxī, sānctum

reach, cōnsequor, cōnsequī, cōnsecūtus sum

read, legō, -ere, lēgī, lēctum

reason, causa, -ae, *f.*

rebuke, reprehendō, -ere, -prehendī, -prehēnsum

receive, accipiō, -ere, -cēpī, -ceptum; recipiō, -ere, recēpī, receptum

red, ruber, rubra, rubrum, *adj.*

regard, aestimō (1)

relationship by marriage, affīnitās, -ātis, *f.*

remain, maneō, -ēre, mānsī, mānsum

remaining, cēterus, -a, -um, *adj.;* reliquus, -a, -um, *adj.*

remember, meminī, meminisse

remembering, memor, -oris, *adj.* + *gen.*

renowned, celeber, -bris, -bre, *adj.*

report, referō, referre, rettulī, relātum

repose, quiēs, -ētis, *f.*

reputation, fāma, -ae, *f.*

require, dēsīderō (1)

resist somebody or something, resistō, -ere, restitī, —, + *dat.*

respect, vereor, verērī, veritus sum

rest, quiēs, -ētis, *f.*

rest, the; the remaining, reliquus, -a, -um, *adj.*

restore, restituō, -ere, restituī, restitūtum

retreat, to, sē recipere

return, redeō, -īre, -īvī, -itum

reveal, dēclārō (1)

reward, praemium, -ī, *n.*

rich, dīves, dīvitis, *adj.*

riches, dīvitiae, -ārum, *f. pl.*

right hand, dextra, -ae, *f.*

right up, ūsque, *adv.*

rising, ortus, -ūs, *m.*

river, flūmen, -minis, *n.*

road, iter, -ineris, *n.;* via, -ae, *f.*

rock, saxum, -ī, *n.*

Roman, Rōmānus, -a, -um, *adj.*

Rome, Rōma, -ae, *f.*

roof, tēctum, -ī, *n.*

rouse, excitō (1)

rub, terō, -ere, trīvī, trītum

rule, imperium, -ī, *n.* (*noun*)

rule, dominor, dominārī, dominātus sum (*verb*)

rumor, fāma, -ae, *f.*

run, currō, -ere, cucurrī, cursum

run away, fugiō, -ere, fūgī, —

rural, rūsticus, -a, -um, *adj.*

rush to, petō, -ere, petīvī, petītum

rustic, rūsticus, -a, -um, *adj.*

S

sad, trīstis, -e, *adj.*

safe, tūtus, -a, -um, *adj.*

sail, nāvigō (1)

sailor, nauta, -ae, *m.*

salt, sāl, salis, *m.*

same, īdem, eadem, idem, *demonstrative pronoun and adj.*

save, servō (1)

say, dīcō, -ere, dīxī, dictum; **I say/I said** (*only introducing direct speech*), inquam

say, s/he says or said (*only introducing direct speech*), inquit

say, they say or said (*only introducing direct speech*), inquiunt

science, ars, artis, *f.*

scream, clāmō (1)

sea, mare, maris, *n.*

search, quaerō, -ere, quaesīvī, quaesītum

seat, sēdēs, -is, *f.*

second, secundus, -a, -um, *adj.*

see, videō, -ēre, vīdī, vīsum; cernō, -ere, crēvī, crētum

seek, petō, -ere, petīvī, petītum

seem, videō, -ēre, vīdī, vīsum (passive)

seize, corripiō, -ere, -ripuī, -reptum

self, ipse, ipsa, ipsum, *demonstrative pronoun and adj.*

send, mittō, -ere, mīsī, missum

send down, dēmittō, -ere, -mīsī, -missum

separate, sēparō (1)

serious, gravis, -e, *adj.;* sevērus, -a, -um, *adj.*

servant, servus, -ī, *m.*

service, beneficium, -ī, *n.*

set up, cōnstituō, -ere, cōnstituī, cōnstitūtum

severe, sevērus, -a, -um, *adj.*

shadows, tenebrae, -ārum, *f. pl.*

shameful, turpis, -e, *adj.*

she, he, it, is, ea, id, *personal and demonstrative pronoun and adj.*

she-wolf, lupa, -ae, *f.*

ship, nāvis, -is, *f.*

shore, lītus, -oris, *n.*

short, brevis, -e, *adj.*

shortly, breviter, *adv.*

should, dēbeō, -ēre, dēbuī, dēbitum, + *inf.*

shout, clāmō (1)

show, dēclārō (1); ostendō, -ere, ostendī, ostentum

sickness, morbus, -ī, *m.*

silent, to be, taceō, -ēre, tacuī, tacitum

silver, argentum, -ī, *n.*

similar, similis, -e, *adj.* + *gen.* or + *dat.*

simultaneously, simul, *adv.*

since, cum, *conj.* + *imperfect subjunctive*

sing, canō, -ere, cecinī, cantum

sister, soror, -ōris, *f.*

sit, sedeō, -ēre, sēdī, sessum

situated, situs, -a, -um, *adj.*

situated in, to be, versor, versārī, versātus sum

situated or occurring at the end, extrēmus, -a, -um, *adj.*

skill, ars, artis, *f.*

skin, pellis, -is, *f.*

sky, caelum, -ī, *n.*

slave, servus, -ī, *m.*

sleep, somnus, -ī, *m.* (*noun*)

sleep, dormiō, -īre, -īvī, -ītum (*verb*)

slender, grācilis, -e, *adj.*

slide, lābor, lābī, lāpsus sum

slip, lābor, lābī, lāpsus sum

small, parvus, -a, -um, *adj.*

smaller, minor, minus, *adj. comparative*

smallest, minimus, -a, -um, *adj. superlative*

smoke, fūmus, -ī, *m.*

snatch away, ēripiō, -ere, -ripuī, -reptum

snow, nix, nivis, *f.*

so, ita, *adv.;* tam, *adv.;* sīc, *adv.*

so . . . as . . ., tam . . . quam . . .

so great, tantus, -a, -um, *adj.*

so many, tot, *adv.*

so much, tantum, *adv.*

so that, ut + *subjunctive*

so that not, nē, *conj.* + *subjunctive*

social class, ōrdō, ōrdinis, *m.*

soldier, mīles, -itis, *m.*

some, aliquis, aliqua, aliquid, *indefinite pronoun;* aliquī, aliqua, aliquod, *indefinite adj.*

sometimes, interdum, *adv.*

somewhat, paulō, *adv.*

son, fīlius, -ī, *m.*

song, carmen, -inis, *n.*

soon, mox, *adv.*

soul, animus, -ī, *m.*

south, merīdiēs, -ēī, *m.*

spare somebody or something, parcō, -ere, pepercī, —, + *dat.*

sparrow, passer, -eris, *m.*

speak, loquor, loquī, locūtus sum

spear, tēlum, -ī, *n.*

speech, ōrātiō, -ōnis, *f.*; **make a speech,** ōrātiōnem habeō

spend time, moror, morārī, morātus sum

spirit, animus, -ī, *m.*; mēns, mentis, *f.*

spouse, coniūnx, -iugis, *m./f.*

stand, stō, -āre, stetī, statum

state, rēs pūblica

stay for a long or short period, moror, morārī, morātus sum

steal, fūror, -ārī, -ātus sum

stick, virga, -ae, *f.*

still, adhūc, *adv.*

stir up, excitō (1)

stone, saxum, -ī, *n.*

stop, dēsinō, -ere, dēsiī, dēsitum

storm, tempestās, -ātis, *f.*; hiems, hiemis, *f.*

story, fābula, -ae, *f.*

stream, rīvus, -ī, *m.*

strength, vīs, —, *f. pl.* vīrēs, vīrium

strengthen, firmō (1)

strict, sevērus, -a, -um, *adj.*

strike, impingō, -ere, impēgī, impāctum; afflīgō, -ere, afflīxī, afflīctum

strike on or against, īnflīgō, -ere, īnflīxī, īnflīctum

strike through, percutiō, -ere, percussī, percussum

strive to achieve, nītor, nītī, nīsus/nīxus sum

strong, fortis, -e, *adj.*

strongly, vehementer, *adv.*

student (*female*), discipula, -ae, *f.*

study, studeō, -ēre, studuī, —, + *dat.*

such a, tālis, tāle, *adj.*

such an extent, to, adeō, *adv.*

suddenly, subitō, *adv.*

suffer, patior, patī, passus sum

sufficiently, satis, *adv.*

sun, sōl, sōlis, *m.*

supply, praestō, -āre, praestitī, praestitum

suppress, opprimō, -ere, oppressī, oppressum

sure, for, prō certō, *adverbial phrase*

sweet, dulcis, -e, *adj.*

sweetness, suāvitās, -ātis, *f.*

swiftly, celeriter, *adv.*

sword, gladius, -ī, *m.*

T

take, capiō, -ere, cēpī, captum; dūcō, -ere, dūxī, ductum; percipiō, -ere, percēpī, perceptum; sūmō, -ere, sūmpsī, sūmptum

take as a wife, uxōrem dūcō

tall, altus, -a, -um, *adj.*

taste (*as in fine judgment and appreciation*), sāl, salis, *m.*

tasteful, ēlegāns, -antis, *adj.*

teach, doceō, -ēre, docuī, doctum

teacher (*male*), magister, magistrī, *m.*

tear, lacrima, -ae, *f.* (*noun*)

tear, rumpō, -ere, rūpī, ruptum (*verb*)

tell, nārrō (1)

temple, aedēs, -is, *f.*; templum, -ī, *n.*

terrifying, terribilis, -e, *adj.*

testimony, testimōnium, -ī, *n.*

than, quam, *used with comparative words*

thankful, grātus, -a, -um, *adj.*

that (*of yours*), iste, ista, istud, *demonstrative pronoun and adj.*

that, ut, *conj.* + *subjunctive*

that, ille, illa, illud, *demonstrative pronoun and adj.*

that, quī, quae, quod, *relative pronoun*

that not, nē, *conj.* + *subjunctive*

theft, fūrtum, -ī, *n.*

their, suus, -a, -um, *possessive adj.*; eōrum

themselves, suī, sibi, sē, *reflexive pronoun*

then, deinde, *adv.*; tum, *adv.*; tunc, *adv.*

there, ibi, *adv.*

therefore, ergō, *conj.*; igitur, *adv.*; quārē, *conj.*

thief, fūr, fūris, *m.*

thing, rēs, reī, *f.*

think, cōgitō (1); exīstimō (1); putō (1)

third, tertius, -a, -um, *adj.*

this, hic, haec, hoc, *demonstrative pronoun and adj.*; is, ea, id, *personal and demonstrative pronoun and adj.*

three, trēs, tria, *numeral*

throng, multitūdō, -ūdinis, *f.*

through, per, *prep.* + *acc.*

throw, iaciō, -ere, iēcī, iactum

thrust back, repellō, -ere, reppulī, repulsum

time, tempus, -oris, *n.*

to, ad, *prep.* + *acc.*; in, *prep.* + *acc.*; ut, *conj.*

today, hodiē, *adv.*

together, ūnā, *adv.*

toil, labor, -ōris, *m.*

tolerate, patior, patī, passus sum

tongue (*as physical part of the mouth*), lingua, -ae, *f.*

too much, nimis, *adj.*

top of, summus, -a, -um, *adj.*

touch, tangō, -ere, tetigī, tāctum

toward, ad, *prep.* + *acc.*

tower, turris, -is, *f.*

town, oppidum, -ī, *n.*

tree, arbor, -oris, *f.*

tribe, gēns, gentis, *f.*

trickery, dolus, -ī, *m.*

trip, iter, itineris, *n.*

true, vērus, -a, -um, *adj.*

try, cōnor, cōnārī, cōnātus sum; temptō (1)

turn, versō (1)

turn round, volvō, -ere, volvī, volūtum

twig, virga, -ae, *f.*

two, duo, duae, dua, *numeral*

type, genus, -eris, *n.*

U

uncle, avunculus, -ī, *m.*

under, sub, *prep.* + *abl.*

understand, intellegō, -ere, intellēxī, intellēctum

undying, immortālis, -e, *adj.*

unjust treatment, iniūria, -ae, *f.*

unless, nisi, *conj.*

unlimited, īnfīnītus, -a, -um, *adj.*

unwilling, to be, nōlō, nōlle, nōluī, —

up to this time, adhūc, *adv.*

up to, ūsque ad + *acc.*

uproar, tumultus, -ūs, *m.*
urge, hortor, hortārī, hortātus sum
use, ūsus, -ūs, *m.* (*noun*)
use, ūtor, ūtī, ūsus sum, + *abl.* (*verb*)
useful, ūtilis, -e, *adj.*

V

vain, in, frūstrā, *adv.*
value, exīstimō (1)
vegetation, herba, -ae, *f.*
vehement, vehemēns, vehementis, *adj.*
vehemently, vehementer, *adv.*
versed in literature, litterātus, -a, -um, *adj.*
very, valdē, *adv.*
very little, minimē, *adv. superlative*
vice, vitium, -ī, *n.*
victor, victor, -ōris, *m.*
villa, vīlla, -ae, *f.*
violent, vehemēns, vehementis, *adj.*
virgin, virgō, -inis, *f.*
virtue, virtūs, -ūtis, *f.*
voice, vōx, vōcis, *f.*
volume, volūmen, -ūminis, *n.*
voyage, nāvigō (1)

W

wage war, bellum gerō
wait for, exspectō (1)
wake up, excitō (1)
walk, ambulō (1)
wall, mūrus, -ī, *m.*
wall-fence, mūrus, -ī, *m.*
wander, errō (1)
want, inopia, -ae, *f.* (*noun*)
want, cupiō, -ere, -īvī, -ītum; volō, velle, voluī, — (*verb*)
want, not to, nōlō, nōlle, nōluī, —
war, bellum, -ī, *n.*
waste, perdō, -ere, perdidī, perditum
watch, spectō (1)
water, aqua, -ae, *f.*
way, modus, -ī, *m.*
way of living, cultus, -ūs, *m.*
we, nōs, *personal pronoun*
wealth, dīvitiae, -ārum, *f. pl.*
weapons, arma, -ōrum, *n. pl.*
wear, gerō, -ere, gessī, gestum
wear out, terō, -ere, trīvī, trītum
weather, caelum, -ī, *n.*
wedding, nūptiae, -ārum, *f. pl.*
weight, onus, oneris, *n.*; pondus, -eris, *n.*; gravitās, -ātis, *f.*
welfare, salūs, -ūtis, *f.*
well, bene, *adv.*
well, to be, valeō, -ēre, valuī, —
well-known, celeber, -bris, -bre, *adj.*
what sort of, quālis, quāle, *interrogative and relative pronoun*
what?, quī, quae, quod?, *interrogative adjective*; quis, quid?, *interrogative pronoun*
wheel, rota, -ae, *f.*
when, cum, *conj.*, + *indicative*; ut + *perfect indicative*
where?, ubi?, *interrogative adv.*
wherefore, quārē, *conj.*
whether . . . or . . ., utrum . . . an . . .
which (of two)?, uter, utra, utrum, *interrogative adj.*
which, quī, quae, quod, *relative pronoun*
which?, quī, quae, quod?, *interrogative adjective*
while, dum, *conj.*
while, for a little, paulisper, *adv.*
white, albus, -a, -um, *adj.*
who, quī, quae, quod, *relative pronoun*
who? quis, quid?, *interrogative pronoun*
who (of two)?, uter, utra, utrum, *interrogative adj.*
whole, tōtus, -a, -um, *adj.*
why?, cūr, *adv.*
wicked, improbus, -a, -um; scelestus, -a, -um, *adj.*
wife, uxor, -ōris, *f.*
will, voluntās, -tātis, *f.*
wind, ventus, -ī, *m.*
wine, vīnum, -ī, *n.*
winter, hiems, hiemis, *f.*
wisdom, prūdentia, -ae, *f.*
wit, sāl, salis, *m.*
with, cum, *prep.* + *abl.*
with all one's might, prō vīribus
with me, mēcum = cum mē
with you, tēcum = cum tē
without, sine, *prep.* + *abl.*
without it being the case that (*after negative clauses*), quīn, *conj.* + *subjunctive*
woman, mulier, -ieris, *f.*; fēmina, -ae, *f.*
wooden, ligneus, -a, -um, *adj.*
word, verbum, -ī, *n.*
world, mundus, -ī, *m.*; orbis terrārum
worse, peior, peius, *adj. comparative*
worship, colō, -ere, coluī, cultum
worst, pessimus, -a, -um, *adj. superlative*
worthwhile, it is, operae pretium est
wound, vulnus, -eris, *n.* (*noun*)
wound, vulnerō (1) (*verb*)
wretched, miser, -a, -um, *adj.*
write, scrībō, -ere, scrīpsī, scrīptum
wrongly, perperam, *adv.*

Y

year, annus, -ī, *m.*
yes, ita, *adv.*
you (pl.), vōs, *personal pronoun*
you (sg.), tū, *personal pronoun*
young man, young lady, adulēscēns, -entis, *m./f.*
your (pl.), vester, vestra, vestrum, *possessive adj.*
your (sg.), tuus, -a, -um, *possessive adj.*
yours (pl.), vester, vestra, vestrum, *possessive adj.*
yours (sg.), tuus, -a, -um, *possessive adj.*
youth, iuventūs, -ūtis, *f.*

LATIN TO ENGLISH GLOSSARY

This glossary contains the **Vocabulary to Learn*** as well as the **Reading Vocabulary** from all the chapters and the Atticus passages.

*All words from the **Vocabulary to Learn** are asterisked. Those from Level 2 are additionally coded: e.g., C12 means the word first appeared as **Vocabulary to Learn** in Chapter 12 while A3 means the word first appeared in the third Atticus selection (those following Chapters 1–15) at the back of the text. In a very few instances, an additional meaning for the word is given in a later part of the text. Such additional meanings appear in the Glossary.

Words marked with a star and no chapter or Atticus selection reference are from the **Vocabulary to Learn** of Level 1.

LIST OF ABBREVIATIONS:

(1) = first conjugation
abl. = ablative
acc. = accusative
adj. = adjective
adv. = adverb
conj. = conjunction
dat. = dative
f. = feminine
gen. = genitive
inf. = infinitive
m. = masculine
n. = neuter
pl. = plural
prep. = preposition
sg. = singular

NOTE:

The genitive of second declension words ending in ***-ius*** or ***-ium*** is indicated with a single ***-ī,*** which is the genitive ending itself. Note that in the full form of the genitive there is normally a double ***i***: *fīlius, -ī* (= *fīliī*); *gaudium, -ī* (= *gaudiī*).

A

ā *or* **ab,** *prep. + abl.,* by, from*

ā sēcrētīs, private secretary

Abaelardus, -ī, *m.,* Abelard

abhorreō, -ēre, abhorruī, —, *+ abl.,* to be averse to, be different from

abiciō, -ere, abiēcī, abiectum, to throw away, cast down

absēns, absentis, *adj.,* away, absent* C13

abstineō, -ēre, abstinuī, abstentum, to keep away; **sē abstinēre,** to abstain

absum, abesse, āfuī, —, to be away*

absurdus, -a, -um, *adj.,* absurd, irrational

abundō (1), *+ abl.,* to abound with*

ac, shortened form of **atque**

ac sī, *conj. + imperfect subjunctive,* as if (*something was happening, which, in fact, was not*)

accēdō, -ere, accessī, accessum, to approach, be added* A10

accelerō (1), to quicken, accelerate

accessiō, -ōnis, *f.,* addition, increase

accidō, -ere, accidī, —, to fall upon, happen* A7

accingō, -ere, accīnxī, accīnctum, to gird on, arm

accipiō, -ere, -cēpī, -ceptum, to accept, receive*

accrēscō, -ere, accrēvī, accrētum, to increase in size

accūsō (1), *+ acc. + gen.,* to accuse someone of something*

ācer, ācris, ācre, *adj.,* keen, fierce*

aciēs, -ēī, *f.,* line of battle, sharp edge

acroāma, acroāmatis, *n.,* any form of entertainment

ad, *prep. + acc.,* toward, to, into*

ad adventum, before the arrival

addō, -ere, addidī, additum, to add* C9

adeō, *adv.,* to such an extent* A8

adhibeō, -ēre, adhibuī, adhibitum, to apply* A10

adhūc, *adv.,* still, up to this time* C8

adiungō, -ere, adiūnxī, adiūnctum, *+ dative* = **iungō**

adiuvō, -āre, adiūvī, adiūtum, to help* A1

admittō, -ere, admīsī, admissum, to admit, let in

adoptō (1), to adopt

adsum, adesse, adfuī, —, to be present

adulēscēns, -entis, *m./f.*, young man, young lady*

adulēscentulus, -ī, *m.*, young man

adūlor, adūlārī, adūlātus sum, to fawn upon, flatter

adventus, -ūs, *m.*, arrival* A2

adversārius, -ī, *m.*, opponent

adversum, *prep. + acc.*, against

aedēs, -is, *f.*, (*in the singular*) a temple; (*in the plural*) a dwelling or house* C10

aedificātor, -ōris, *m.*, builder; *adj.*, devoted to building

aedificium, -ī, *n.*, building* A5

aedificō (1), to build*

aemulātiō, aemulātiōnis, *f.*, emulation, envy

Aenēās, Aenēae, *m.*, Aeneas

aequālis, aequāle, *adj.*, equal, contemporary in age

aequālis, -is, *m./f.*, a person of the same age

aequus, -a, -um, *adj.*, even, fair; **aequō animō,** indifferently*

aerārium, -ī, *n.*, treasury, fund, account

aes, aeris, *n.*, bronze

aestās, -ātis, *f.*, summer; **aestāte,** in the summer

aestimō (1), to regard, esteem; **aestimō ūnīus assis,** I do not care a bit*

aestuō (1), to be in violent commotion, burn

aetās, -ātis, *f.*, age* C7

affectō (1), to try to achieve, strive after

afferō, afferre, attulī, allātum, to bring

affīnitās, -ātis, *f.*, relationship by marriage, connection* A9

affirmō (1), to assert, maintain* C14

afflīgō, -ere, -flīxī, -flīctum, to strike, distress, afflict* A3

affluentia, -ae, *f.*, opulence, extravagance

ager, agrī, *m.*, field*

agmen, -minis, *n.*, marching column* C4

agō, -ere, ēgī, āctum, to drive, lead, do, behave*

agricola, -ae, *m.*, farmer*

albus, -a, -um, *adj.*, white*

aliēnus, -a, -um, *adj. + prep. ā/ab + abl.*, foreign to, inconsistent with*

aliī . . . aliī . . ., some . . . others . . .

aliquis, aliqua, aliquid, *indefinite pronoun*; **aliquī, aliqua, aliquod,** *indefinite adj.*, some* A6

aliquot, *indeclinable indefinite pronoun and adj.*, some, a few

alius, alia, aliud, *adj.*, another, other*

alō, -ere, aluī, altum/alitum, to feed, nourish*

alter, altera, alterum, *adj.*, the other (of two)* C11

alteruter, alterutra, alterutrum, *adj.*, either of two

altus, -a, -um, *adj.*, tall, deep* C2

amāritūdō, amāritūdinis, *f.*, bitterness

amātor, -ōris, *m.*, lover

ambitus, -ūs, *m.*, bribery to obtain office

ambulō (1), to walk*

amīca, -ae, *f.*, friend

amīcitia, -ae, *f.*, friendship

amīcus, -a, -um, *adj.*, friendly* A1

amīcus, -ī, *m.*, friend*

āmittō, -ere, -mīsī, -missum, to lose*

amō (1), to love*

amoenitās, -ātis, *f.*, pleasantness (*of a place*)

amor, -ōris, *m.*, love*

amplitūdō, amplitūdinis, *f.*, size, importance

amplius, *adv.*, a greater amount, a greater number, more* A8

an, or (*in a disjunctive question*)

anagnōstēs, -ae, *m.*, reader, slave whose job is to read aloud

ancilla, -ae, *f.*, female servant, maidservant

Andrēas (-ae) Ammōnius, -ī, *m.*, Andrew Ammonius, Italian in origin, secretary to the British King Henry VIII, and friend of Erasmus

Anemōliī, -ōrum, *m. pl.*, the Anemolians, the name of a fictional population

Anglī, -ōrum, *m. pl.*, the English

Anglus, -a, -um, *adj.*, English

animadvertō, -ere, animadvertī, animadversum, to notice* C15

animal, -ālis, *n.*, animal*

animus, -ī, *m.*, spirit, soul, mind*

anniculus, -a, -um, *adj.*, one year long, yearling

annuō, -ere, annuī, annūtum, to nod, grant, approve

annus, -ī, *m.*, year* C2

ante, *adv.*, before

ante, *prep. + acc.*, in front of*

antīquitās, -ātis, *f.*, antiquity, ancient tradition* A9

antīquitus, *adv.*, from old times

antīquus, -a, -um, *adj.*, ancient* C8

ānulus, -ī, *m.*, ring

anxius, -a, -um, *adj.*, anxious, worried

aperiō, -īre, aperuī, apertum, to open* C4

appāreō, -ēre, appāruī, —, to appear, be found* A7

appāret, -ēre, it is clear, obvious

appellō (1), to call upon, name, address

apprīmē, *adv.*, to the highest degree, especially

appropinquō (1), to approach* C15

aptus, -a, -um, *adj.*, fitted, appropriate* A7

apud, *prep. + acc.*, at the house of*

aqua, -ae, *f.*, water*

Aquīsgrānum, -ī, *n.*, Aachen (Aix-la-Chapelle), a town in western Germany, with mineral waters (as the name indicates), a seat of the Holy Roman Empire

arbitror, arbitrārī, arbitrātus sum, to judge, consider, be of the opinion, suppose* A6

arbor, -oris, *f.*, tree*

arcessō, -ere, arcessīvī, arcessītum, to send for, fetch

ārdeō, -ēre, ārsī, —, to burn, be on fire*

argentum, -ī, *n.*, silver* C2

argūmentum, -ī, *n.*, proof, indication, argument*

arma, -ōrum, *n. pl.*, weapons*

armātus, -a, -um, *adj.*, armed*

Arrētīnus, -a, -um, *adj.*, connected with Arrētium, a town in Etruria

ars, artis, *f.*, science, art, skill* C8

artifex, -ficis, *m.*, craftsman, artisan* A5

arx, arcis, *f.*, citadel

ascendō, -ere, ascendī, ascēnsum, to climb

ascīscō, -ere, ascīvī, ascītum, to receive, adopt, summon from elsewhere

ascrībō, -ere, ascrīpsī, ascrīptum, to impute, ascribe, attribute

Āsia, -ae, *f.*, Asia

asperitās, asperitātis, *f.*, harshness

aspiciō, -ere, aspexī, aspectum, to look at, catch a glimpse of* C1

assecla, -ae, *m.*, follower, attendant

assiduus, -a, -um, *adj.*, diligent, dedicated

assus, -a, -um, *adj.*, roasted

at, *conj.*, but* C3

Athēnae, -ārum, *f. pl.*, Athens

Athēniēnsēs, Athēniēnsium, *m. pl.*, the Athenians

āthlēta, -ae, *m.*, athlete*

atque, *conj.*, and*

attingō, -ere, attigī, attāctum, to touch, engage in

audiō, -īre, audīvī, audītum, to hear, listen*

augeō, -ēre, auxī, auctum, to increase* A4

Augustīnus, -ī, *m.*, Augustine

aureus, -a, -um, *adj.*, golden

auris, -is, *f.*, ear* C9

aurum, -ī, *n.*, gold* C2

aut, *conj.*, or; **aut . . . aut . . .,** either . . . or . . .* A2

autem, *conj.*, however, on the other hand

auxilium, -ī, *n.*, help*

avidē, *adv.*, eagerly, greedily

avis, -is, *f.*, bird

avunculus, -ī, *m.*, uncle*

axis, -is, *m.*, axle, axis*

B

bālaena, -ae, *f.*, whale

barba, -ae, *f.*, beard*

barbarus, -ī, *m.*, barbarian; foreign, uneducated

beātus, -a, -um, *adj.*, blessed

bellum, -ī, *n.*, war*

bene, *adv.*, well*

beneficium, -ī, *n.*, service, kindness, favor, benefit* A3

benevolentia, -ae, *f.*, good will* C13

bibō, -ere, bibī, —, to drink* C5

bīduum, -ī, *n.*, a period of two days; **bīduum,** for two days

bonitās, bonitātis, *f.*, moral excellence, goodness

bonum pūblicum, -ī, *n.*, the public good

bonus, -a, -um, *adj.*, good*

Britannia, -ae, *f.*, Britain

Britō, Britonis, *m.*, a Briton

brevis, -e, *adj.*, short* C2

breviter, *adv.*, shortly, briefly* A8

Brūtī, the conspirators Marcus Brutus and Decimus Brutus

C

C. = Gāius, Roman first name

C. Flāvius, -ī, *m.*, a close friend of Brutus

cacūmen, -ūminis, *n.*, top

cadō, -ere, cecidī, cāsum, to fall*

caelestis, -e, *adj.*, celestial

caelum, -ī, *n.*, sky, heaven, weather*

Caesar, -aris, *m.*, emperor (initially the name of Julius Caesar), Caesar* A4

Caesariānus, -a, -um, *adj.*, of Caesar

calamitās, -ātis, *f.*, disaster, misfortune, calamity* A1

calēns, calentis, *adj.*, hot; **aquae nātūrāliter calentēs,** hot water springs

callidus, -a, -um, *adj.*, clever, cunning

canō, -ere, cecinī, cantum, to sing* A7

cānus, -a, -um, *adj.*, gray (for hair)

capillus, -ī, *m.*, hair

capiō, -ere, cēpī, captum, to take, adopt, capture; **cōnsilia capere,** to make plans*

capulus, -ī, *m.*, handle, hilt

caput, -itis, *n.*, head*

carmen, -inis, *n.*, poem, song* C5

carō, carnis, *f.*, meat, flesh*

Carolus, -ī, *m.*, Charles

cārus, -a, -um, *adj.*, dear* C12

casa, -ae, *f.*, little house, cottage*

castra, -ōrum, *n. pl.*, camp*

cāsus, -ūs, *m.*, accident, chance occurrence

Catilīna, -ae, *m.*, Catiline, a bankrupt revolutionary whose plot to overthrow the Republic was exposed by Cicero

causa, -ae, *f.*, cause, reason, case*

cēdō, -ere, cessī, cessum, to go away (from), withdraw, move

celeber, -bris, -bre, *adj.*, renowned, well-known, crowded*

celeritās, -ātis, *f.*, speed

celeriter, *adv.*, swiftly*

cēlō (1), to hide

cēnō (1), to dine* A6

centiēs sēstertium, ten million sesterces (in Roman currency)

centrum, -ī, *n.*, center

centum, *numeral and indeclinable adj.*, one hundred

Cerēs, Cereris, *f.*, goddess of grain and agriculture (in Greek, Demeter)

cernō, -ere, crēvī, crētum, to see, distinguish by the eyes* C15

cervīx, cervīcis, *f.*, neck

cēterus, -a, -um, *adj.*, other, remaining; *in pl.*, the rest* A5

cibus, -ī, *m.*, food* C5

cinis, -eris, *m.*, ash*

Cinna, -ae, *m.* Cinna, leader in Roman civil wars of first century CE

Cinnānus, -a, -um, *adj.*, related to **Cinna, -ae,** *m.*

circā, *prep.* + *acc.*, around* C15

circiter, *adv.*, approximately, around

circulāris, -e, *adj.*, circular

circum, *prep.* + *acc.*, around*

circumeō, -īre, -īvī, -itum, to go around* C14

cīvīlis, -e, *adj.*, civil, pertaining to the state

cīvis, -is, *m./f.*, citizen*

cīvitās, cīvitātis, *f.*, city, community of citizens, state, political entity

clādēs, -is, *f.*, disaster*

clam, *adv.*, secretly

clāmō (1), to scream* C15

clārus, -a, -um, *adj.*, clear, distinguished* C2

classis, -is, *f.*, fleet*

clāvis, -is, *f.*, key

coeō, coīre, coīvī, coitum, to come together, meet

coepī, coepisse, coeptum, + *inf.*, to begin to* C4

cōgitō (1), to think*

cognōscō, -ere, cognōvī, cognitum, to come to know, find to be* A1

cōgō, -ere, coēgī, coactum, to compel, force* A5

colaphus, -ī, *m.*, slap, blow with a fist

collaudō, -āre, -āvī, -ātum, to praise warmly

collis, -is, *m.*, hill* A5

collocō (1), to set up, give in marriage

colloquor, colloquī, collocūtus sum, to converse

colō, -ere, coluī, cultum, to worship, cultivate*

Colōnus, -ī, *m.,* Columbus

coma, -ae, *f.,* hair

comedō, -ere, -ēdī, -ēsum, to eat*

comes, comitis, *m.,* count; companion, associate

Comes Flandrēnsium, Robert II, Count of Flanders (a region of Belgium today), one of the principal generals in the First Crusade

Comes Tolōsānus, Raymond IV, count of Toulouse (in southern France), one of the leaders of the First Crusade

cōmitās, -ātis, *f.,* friendliness, courtesy

commemorō (1), to recall

committō, -ere, commīsī, commissum, to entrust

commoditās, commoditātis, *f.,* advantage, convenience

commūtō (1), to change (completely)

compleō, -ēre, -ēvī, -ētum, to fill, complete* A10

complūrēs, complūrium, *adj.,* not a few, several

concēdō, -ere, concessī, concessum, to allow, pardon

conciliātor, -ōris, *m.,* mediator

conciliō (1), to bring together

condiciō, -ōnis, *f.,* condition, terms of a loan or agreement* A4

condiscipulātus, -ūs, *m.,* companionship at school

condiscipulus, -ī, *m.,* classmate

cōnferō, cōnferre, cōntulī, cōllātum, to compare, bring together, collect, contribute

cōnfessiō, -ōnis, *f.,* confession

cōnficiō, -ere, cōnfēcī, cōnfectum, to make, compose

coniūnctiō, -ōnis, *f.,* connection

coniūnctissimē, *adv.,* in a very friendly manner

coniungō, -ere, -iūnxī, -iūnctum, to connect, join together* A4

coniūnx, -iugis, *m./f.,* spouse* C3

cōnor, cōnārī, cōnātus sum, to try* C9

cōnsēnsiō, cōnsēnsiōnis, *f.,* agreement

cōnsequor, cōnsequī, cōnsecūtus sum, to acquire, gain* A9

cōnservō (1), to preserve

cōnsilium, -ī, *n.,* plan, advice*

consōbrīna, -ae, *f.,* cousin

cōnspiciō, -ere, -spexī, -spectum, to look at, observe*

cōnstantia, -ae, *f.,* constancy*

cōnstituō, -ere, cōnstituī, cōnstitūtum, to establish, set up, institute, decide* A4

cōnstō, -āre, cōnstitī, —, + *abl.,* to consist in* A5

cōnsuētūdō, -ūdinis, *f.,* custom, habit, companionship* A6

cōnsul, -ulis, *m.,* consul*

cōnsulātus, -ūs, *m.,* consulship

cōnsulō, -ere, cōnsuluī, cōnsultum, + *dat.,* to look after; + *acc.,* to consult* A10

cōnsultō, *adv.,* on purpose

cōnsūmō, -ere, -sūmpsī, -sūmptum, to consume*

contemnō, -ere, contempsī, contemptum, to regard with contempt, despise* A10

cōntentiō, -ōnis, *f.,* contest, fight

contentus, -a, -um, *adj.,* + *abl.,* contented with, content

contexō, -ere, contexuī, contextum, to join by weaving, compose

contineō, -ēre, continuī, contentum, to hold, keep together, contain* C14

contrā, *prep.* + *acc.,* against*

conveniō, -īre, convēnī, conventum, to meet; + *dat.,* to be becoming to, be appropriate for*

convertō, -ere, convertī, conversum, to rotate, invert, turn

convictus, -ūs, *m.,* social relationships, a living together

convīva, -ae, *m./f.,* dinner companion, guest

convīvium, -ī, *n.,* dinner party, feast* A6

cōpula, -ae, *f.,* bond, connection

coquō, -ere, coxī, coctum, to cook*

cor, cordis, *n.,* heart*

cornū, -ūs, *n.,* horn*

corpus, -oris, *n.,* body*

corripiō, -ere, -ripuī, -reptum, to seize*

corrumpō, -ere, corrūpī, corrūptum, to corrupt

cottīdiānus, -a, -um, *adj.,* daily, of every day* C14

crēdō, -ere, crēdidī, crēditum, + *dat.,* to believe somebody, lend money*

crēscō, -ere, crēvī, —, to grow*

crīmen, crīminis, *n.,* crime, illegal action

crista, -ae, *f.,* a tuft on the head of animals; **cristās ērigere,** to carry the head high, be conceited

crūdēlis, -e, *adj.,* cruel*

cubitum, -ī, *n.,* elbow

cultor, -ōris, *m.,* fosterer, supporter, cultivator

cultus, -ūs, *m.,* care, management, maintenance, way of living* A6

cum, *conj.,* + *indicative,* when; + *imperfect subjunctive,* although, since; + *pluperfect subjunctive,* after* C12

cum, *prep.* + *abl.,* with*

cupiditās, -ātis, *f.,* greed, immoderate desire

cupiō, -ere, -īvī, -ītum, to desire, want*

cūr, *adv.,* why?*

cūra, -ae, *f.,* care* A6

cūrō (1), to care for, take care of*

currō, -ere, cucurrī, cursum, to run*

cursus, -ūs, *m.,* course, direction, way, going

custōs, -ōdis, *m.,* guard* C2

D

Dalmatia, -ae, *f.,* region of the Roman Empire next to Illyricum on the east coast of the Adriatic Sea. It corresponds in part to the area today called Croatia.

dē, *prep.* + *abl.,* about, concerning; down from, from*

dea, -ae, *f.,* goddess*

dēbeō, -ēre, dēbuī, dēbitum, + *inf.,* ought, must, should; to owe*

dēcēdō, -ere, dēcessī, dēcessum, to go away, die, withdraw* A10

dēcernō, -ere, -crēvī, -crētum, + *inf.,* to decide, determine*

decet, decēre (*impersonal verb*), it is becoming

dēcipiō, -ere, dēcēpī, dēceptum, to deceive* C6

dēclārō (1), to demonstrate, indicate, show* C13

dēdūcō, -ere, dēdūxī, dēductum, to lead away

dēfendō, -ere, dēfendī, dēfēnsum, to defend* C4

dehortor, dehortārī, dehortātus sum, to discourage, dissuade

deinde, *adv.,* then*

dēlectō (1), to delight, please*

dēleō, -ēre, dēlēvī, dēlētum, to destroy*

dēliciae, -ārum, *f. pl.,* delight, pet*

dēligō, -ere, dēlēgī, dēlectum, to choose

delphīn, delphīnis, *m.,* dolphin

dēmittō, -ere, -mīsī, -missum, to send down; **animum dēmittō,** to let my spirit sink, become dejected* C9

dēprecor, dēprecārī, dēprecātus sum, to try to avert (by prayer)

dēprimō, -ere, dēpressī, dēpressum, to repress

dēscendō, -ere, -scendī, -scēnsum, to descend*

dēscrībō, -ere, dēscrīpsī, dēscrīptum, to describe

dēsīderium, -ī, *n.,* grief for something absent

dēsīderō (1), to long for, desire, need, require* A7

dēsinō, -ere, dēsiī, dēsitum, to stop* A10

dēspērātus, -a, -um, *adj.,* desperate

dēspērō (1), to despair

dēspiciō, -ere, dēspexī, dēspectum, to despise

dēspondeō, -ēre, dēspondī, dēspōnsum, to promise a woman in marriage, betroth

dēsum, dēesse, dēfuī, —, to be absent, fail

dētrahō, -ere, dētrāxī, dētrāctum, to take off, take away, detract from

dētrīmentum, -ī, *n.,* damage, detriment

deus, -ī, *m.,* god*

dēvastō (1), to devastate*

dēvinciō, -īre, dēvīnxī, dēvīnctum, to tie up, oblige, attach

dextra, -ae, *f.,* right hand*

dīcō, -ere, dīxī, dictum, to say*

diēs, -ēī, *m./f.,* day*

difficilis, -e, *adj.,* difficult*

digitus, -ī, *m.,* finger*

dignitās, dignitātis, *f.,* dignity, status, social position

dīligēns, dīligentis, *adj.,* diligent

dīligenter, *adv.,* diligently, carefully* A8

dīligentia, -ae, *f.,* carefulness, attentiveness, diligence* A1

dīligō, -ere, dīlēxī, dīlēctum, to esteem highly, love* C6

dīmittō, -ere, dīmīsī, dīmissum, to send away

dīrigō, -ere, dīrexī, dīrectum, to guide, direct, aim, send

discēdēns, discēdentis, *participle,* leaving

discēdō, -ere, -cessī, -cessum, to leave*

discipula, -ae, *f.,* student (female)* C3

discō, -ere, didicī, —, to learn* C3

disiciō, -ere, disiēcī, disiectum, to break up and scatter

dissēnsiō, dissēnsiōnis, *f.,* disagreement

dissimilis, -e, *adj.,* dissimilar* C9

dissipō (1), to scatter, disperse

distineō, -ēre, distinuī, distentum, to hold apart, distract

dītī = dīvite

diū, *adv.,* for a long time*

dīves, dīvitis, *adj.,* rich*

dīvīnātiō, dīvīnātiōnis, *f.,* prophecy, divination, foreseeing, predicting the future

dīvīnus, -a, -um, *adj.,* divine*

dīvitiae, -ārum, *f. pl.,* wealth, riches*

dīvus, -ī, *m.,* god, deified emperor

dō, dăre, dedī, dătum, to give*

doceō, -ēre, docuī, doctum, to teach*

docilitās, docilitātis, *f.,* aptness for being taught, docility

doctrīna, -ae, *f.,* learning, erudition

doctus, -a, -um, *adj.,* learned*

doleō, -ēre, doluī, —, to feel pain, hurt*

dolor, -ōris, *m.,* grief, pain*

dolus, -ī, *m.,* trickery, deception*

domesticus, -a, -um, *adj.,* domestic

domī, at home*

domicilium, -ī, *n.,* dwelling, abode

domina, -ae, *f.,* mistress*

dominātus, -ūs, *m.,* rule, sovereignty

dominor, dominārī, dominātus sum, to dominate, rule* C8

dominus, -ī, *m.,* master, lord* C3

domus, -ūs, *f.,* house, home*

dōnō (1), to give, bestow; + *acc.* + *abl.,* to present someone with something

dōnum, -ī, *n.,* gift*

dormiō, -īre, -īvī, -ītum, to sleep*

Drūsillā, -ae, *f.,* Livia Drusilla, a powerful Roman matron, mother of the emperor Tiberius; later a wife of Octavian Augustus

ducentī, -ae, -a, *adj.,* two hundred

dūcō, -ere, dūxī, ductum, to lead, take*

dulcis, -e, *adj.,* sweet* C5

dum, *conj.,* while; + *subjunctive,* until*

duo, duae, dua, *numeral,* two* C6

dux, ducis, *m.,* leader, general (in medieval Latin often means "duke")*

E

ē *or* **ex,** *prep.* + *abl.,* from, out of*

ē contrāriō, on the contrary

ē rē pūblicā, in accord with the public good

ēbrius, -a, -um, *adj.,* drunk

ecce, *interj.,* look here!*

ēdō, -ere, ēdidī, ēditum, to produce, give forth* C4

efficiō, -ere, -fēcī, -fectum, *often* + *ut,* to cause to happen, bring about, effect, to bring to effect, to accomplish* A4

effugiō, -ere, effūgī, —, to escape

effūsus, -a, -um, *adj.,* lavish, unrestrained

egeō, -ēre, eguī, —, + *abl.,* to lack something*

ego, *personal pronoun,* I*

egomet, *pronoun,* I myself

ēlegāns, -antis, *adj.,* careful in choosing, tasteful* A5

ēlegantia, -ae, *f.,* fineness of taste, elegance

elementum, -ī, *n.,* element* C14

ēliciō, -ere, ēlicuī, ēlicitum, to coax, entice, elicit, call forth

ēlixus, -a, -um, *adj.,* boiled

ēloquentia, -ae, *f.,* eloquence

emāx, emācis, *adj.,* fond of buying

ēmergō, -ere, ēmersī, ēmersum, to come out of the water, emerge

emō, -ere, ēmī, ēmptum, to buy* A1

ēn, *interj.,* see there!

enim, *conj.,* for, in fact*

eō, *adv.,* for that reason

eō, īre, īvī, itum, to go* C10

eōdem, *adv.,* to the same place

epistula, -ae, *f.,* letter*

eques, -itis, *m.,* horseman, knight, member of the equestrian order* C2

equester, -tris, -tre, *adj.,* equestrian, related to the social class of knights; **ōrdō equester,** the order of the knights (the social class between patricians and plebeians)

equitēs, -itum, *m. pl.,* the order of knights (middle rank in Roman society)

equus, -ī, *m.,* horse*

Erasmus (-ī) Roterodamus, -ī, *m.,* Erasmus of Rotterdam

ergō, *conj.,* therefore* C14

ērigō, -ere, ērēxī, ērēctum, to raise, set up

ēripiō, -ere, -ripuī, -reptum, to snatch away*

errō (1), to wander, make a mistake*

ērudiō, -īre, ērudīvī, ērudītum, to educate, instruct

et, *conj.,* and; **et . . . et . . .,** both . . . and . . .* C1

etiam, *adv.,* even, also*

etsī, *conj.,* although* A2

Eurōpa, -ae, *f.,* Europe

ex *or* **ē,** *prep. + abl.,* from, out of*

ex dōdrante, from a portion of three-quarters

excellenter, *adv.,* in an excellent way

excitō (1), to awaken, wake up, rouse, stir up*

exclāmō (1), to exclaim*

excōgitō (1), to think up, devise

exemplar, -āris, *n.,* example*

exemplum, -ī, *n.,* example*

exercitus, -ūs, *m.,* army* C6

eximō, -ere, exēmī, exēmptum, to take out, remove

exīstimō (1), to value, esteem, think, deem, suppose, consider* A1

expers, -ertis, *adj., + gen.,* having no share in, devoid of, free from* A8

expōnō, -ere, exposuī, expositum, to set forth in words, describe, explain, relate about

exsilium, -ī, *n.,* exile

exspectō (1), to wait for, await, expect*

exsplendēscō, -ere, exsplenduī, —, to shine forth, be famous

exstinguō, -ere, -stīnxī, -stīnctum, to extinguish*

externus, -a, -um, *adj.,* outward, external*

extrā, *prep. + acc.,* outside of* C4

extrēmus, -a, -um, *adj.,* situated or occurring at the end, last* A7

F

fābula, -ae, *f.,* story*

faciēs, -ēī, *f.,* face*

facile, *adv.,* easily*

facilis, -e, *adj.,* easy* C9

facilitās, -ātis, *f.,* an easy, good nature

faciō, -ere, fēcī, factum, to do, make*

factiō, factiōnis, *f.,* political preference, party

factum, -ī, *n.,* fact, action

facultās, facultātis, *f.,* ability; *f. pl.,* resources, riches

faenus, -oris, *n.,* interest, profit

falsus, -a, -um, *adj.,* false

fāma, -ae, *f.,* fame, name* C3

familia, -ae, *f.,* family, household*

familiāris, -āris, *m./f.,* family member, a family member or relation* A1

familiāris, familiāre, *adj.,* belonging to the same family, intimate person or thing

familiāritās, -ātis, *f.,* familiarity* A1

familiās, *archaic gen. sing. of familia,* of the family

fastīgium, -ī, *n.,* highest part, roof, top

fātum, -ī, *n.,* fate, destiny*

faveō, -ēre, fāvī, fautum *+ dat.,* to favor

febris, -is, *f.,* fever* A10

fēlīx, -īcis, *adj.,* fortunate, happy*

fēmina, -ae, *f.,* woman*

ferō, ferre, tulī, lātum, to carry, bear, endure* C9

ferōx, -ōcis, *adj.,* fierce, ferocious*

ferrum, -ī, *n.,* iron

fidēlis, -e, *adj.,* faithful, loyal*

fidēs, -eī, *f.,* faith* C7

fīlia, -ae, *f.,* daughter*

fīlius, -ī, *m.,* son*

findō, -ere, fidī, fissum, to split

fingō, -ere, fīnxī, fictum, to imagine, form in the mind* C15

fīnis, -is, *m.,* end* C2

fīō, fierī, factus sum, to be made, become; *(impersonally)* to happen* C9

firmō (1), to strengthen*

flamma, -ae, *f.,* flame*

fleō, -ēre, flēvī, flētum, to cry* A10

flō (1), to blow

flōreō, -ēre, flōruī, —, to blossom, flourish* A3

fluctus, -ūs, *m.,* wave, breaker

flūmen, -minis, *n.,* river* C5

fluō, -ere, flūxī, fluxum, to flow*

fodiō, -ere, fōdī, fossum, to dig; **latus fodere,** to stab someone's side with an elbow

folium, -ī, *n.,* leaf

forīs, *adv.,* outside, in the open*

fōrma, -ae, *f.,* form, appearance*

fortasse, *adv.,* perhaps*

fortis, -e, *adj.,* brave, strong*

fortitūdō, -inis, *f.,* courage*

fortūna, -ae, *f.,* fortune, the goddess Fortune; *f. pl.,* financial resources*

forum, -ī, *n.,* Forum Rōmānum, the main square in Rome* A2

Francī, -ōrum, *m. pl.,* the Franks

Franciscus (-ī) Petrarca, -ae, *m.,* Francis Petrarch (His name in Italian is Francesco Petrarca.)

Francus, -ī, *m.,* a Frank

frāter, frātris, *m.,* brother* C3

frequēns, -entis, *adj.,* frequent, assiduous* A9

frīgus, -oris, *n.,* cold* C9

frūctus, -ūs, *m.,* fruit, gain, profit, revenue

frūmentum, -ī, *n.,* grain

fruor, fruī, fruitus/frūctus sum, *+ abl.,* to enjoy, enjoy the society of* C10

frūstrā, *adv.,* in vain, to no avail* A10

frūx, frūgis, *f.,* crop, produce of the earth

fuga, -ae, *f.,* flight

fugiō, -ere, fūgī, —, to flee, run away*

fulgeō, -ēre, fulsī, —, to shine

fūmus, -ī, *m.,* smoke*

fundō, -ere, fūdī, fūsum, to pour* C7

fundus, -ī, *m.,* country estate, farm

fūnestus, -a, -um, *adj.,* deadly*

fūnis, -is, *m.,* rope

fūr, fūris, *m.,* thief*

furō, -ere, furuī, —, to rage, be insane* C4

fūror, fūrārī, fūrātus sum, to steal* C10

furor, -ōris, *m.,* madness, fury

fūrtum, -ī, *n.,* theft*

futūrus, -a, -um, *participle,* about to be*

G

Galilaeus, -ī, *m.,* Galileo

Gallī, -ōrum, *m. pl.,* the Gauls, the inhabitants of France

Gallia, -ae, *f.,* Gaul, a region of modern France

Gallia Belgica, -ae, *f.,* Belgium

gaudium, -ī, *n.,* joy*

gemma, -ae, *f.,* gem, precious stone* C11

gener, generī, *m.,* son-in-law

generō (1), to give birth, procreate; *pass.,* to descend from

generōsus, -a, -um, *adj.,* highborn, of noble birth

gēns, gentis, *f.,* tribe, population* C1

genū, genūs, *n.,* knee

genus, -eris, *n.,* type, kind* C9

Germānia, -ae, *f.,* the region of Europe approximately corresponding to modern Germany

gerō, -ere, gessī, gestum, to carry, wear; "to administer" in civil politics; **sē gerit,** s/he behaves; **bellum gerō,** to wage war* C2

gesta, -ōrum, *n. pl.,* deeds

gignō, -ere, genuī, genitum, to produce, give birth* C1

glaciēs, -ēī, *f.,* ice* C9

gladius, -ī, *m.,* sword*

globus, -ī, *m.,* mass, association of men, band

glōria, -ae, *f.,* glory* C7

Godefrīdus, -ī, *m.,* Godfrey of Bouillon

Golia, -ae, *m.,* name of a wandering scholar

grācilis, -e, *adj.,* slender* C9

gradior, gradī, gressus sum, to walk

Graecē, *adv.,* in Greek

grandō, grandinis, *f.,* hail

grātia, -ae, *f.,* agreeableness, favor, grace; winning character, influence* A4

grātus, -a, -um, *adj.,* thankful, appreciative, gratifying* A1

gravis, -e, *adj.,* heavy, serious* C2

gravitās, -ātis, *f.,* weight, gravity* C14

gremium, -ī, *n.,* bosom, lap*

gubernātor, -ōris, *m.,* helmsman, pilot

Guilhelmus (-ī) Montoius, -ī, *m.,* William Mountjoy

H

habeō, -ēre, habuī, habitum, to have*

habitō (1), to live, dwell*

habuit cognitam = cognōvit

hastīle, hastīlis, *n.,* shaft

haud, *adv.,* not

Heloīsa, -ae, *f.,* Heloise

herba, -ae, *f.,* plant, vegetation*

hērēditās, -ātis, *f.,* inheritance* A5

hērēs, -ēdis, *m./f.,* heir* C6

heu, *interj.,* alas!

Hibernia, -ae, *f.,* Ireland

hīc, *adv.,* here

hic, haec, hoc, *demonstrative pronoun and adj.,* this*

hiems, hiemis, *f.,* winter, storm* A2

Hierosolyma, -ōrum, *n. pl.,* Jerusalem

Hispānia, -ae, *f.,* Spain

Hispānus, -a, -um, *adj.,* Spaniard

historia, -ae, *f.,* history, written account of past events

historicus, -ī, *m.,* historian

hodiē, *adv.,* today* C1

homō, -inis, *m.,* man (*i.e., human being*); *pl.,* people*

honor, -ōris, *m.,* honor, public office or distinction*

hortor, hortārī, hortātus sum, to exhort, urge* C8

hortus, -ī, *m.,* garden* A6

hostis, -is, *m.,* enemy*

HS, an abbreviation for *sestertiōrum,* sesterces

hūc, *adv.,* to this place, hither

hūmānitās, -ātis, *f.,* human character, kindness; culture, humanity, refinement befitting a man* A7

hūmānus, -a, -um, *adj.,* human*

humilis, -e, *adj.,* low* C9

I

iaceō, -ēre, iacuī, —, to lie down, be inert*

iaciō, -ere, iēcī, iactum, to throw*

iam, *adv.,* already; anymore*

ibi, *adv.,* there*

id est, namely, that is to say (*a common phrase used to make a previous assertion more specific*)

īdem, eadem, idem, *demonstrative pronoun and adj.,* the same* C13

i.e. = id est

igitur, *adv.,* therefore*

ignis, -is, *m.,* fire*

ignōrō (1), to have no knowledge, be ignorant of

ille, illa, illud, *demonstrative pronoun and adj.,* that*

illūstris, -e, *adj.,* distinguished, illustrious* A8

Illyricum, -ī, *n.,* a region situated on the west coast of what is today the Balkan peninsula

imāgō, -inis, *f.,* image* A8

imitātor, -ōris, *m.,* imitator, emulator

immemor, -oris, *adj.,* + *gen.,* forgetful of* C5

immēnsus, -a, -um, *adj.,* immeasurable, immense, endless* C14

immō, *conj.,* on the contrary, nay rather

immortālis, -e, *adj.,* undying, immortal* A3

impediō, -īre, -īvī, -ītum, to impede, prevent* A10

imperātor, -ōris, *m.,* emperor, general, commanding officer* A2

imperium, -ī, *n.,* rule, power, empire, dominion, command* C6

impertiō, -īre, impertīvī, impertītum, to share, provide (to give a *pars*)

impetus, -ūs, *m.,* impetus, force, attack*

impingō, -ere, impēgī, impāctum, to push, strike, drive into* C15

implicō, -āre, implicuī, implicitum/ implicātum, + *dat.,* to involve into, implicate

improbus, -a, -um, *adj.,* bad, wicked* C3

in, *prep.* + *abl.,* in, on*

in, *prep.* + *acc.,* in, into, toward (*when referring to feelings or attitude to someone*)*

in aeternum, forever

in diem, for a future day

in diēs, daily, as the days proceed

in prīmīs (imprīmīs), especially, above all, first of all

incendium, -ī, *n.,* conflagration, eruption*

incendō, -ere, incendī, incēnsum, to set fire, irritate

incidō, -ere, incidī, incāsum, to fall into

incitō (1), to stimulate, instigate

incola, -ae, *m.,* inhabitant* C1

incolumitās, -ātis, *f.,* freedom from harm, safety

incommodum, -ī, *n.,* disadvantage, harm* A4

indicium, -ī, *n.,* indication

indicō (1), to show, indicate

indigeō, -ēre, indiguī, —, + *abl.,* to need, lack* A10

indignus, -a, -um, *adj.,* + *dat.,* unworthy of

indīligēns, indīligentis, *adj.,* careless, negligent

indulgeō, -ēre, indulsī, indultum, + *dat.,* to be indulgent, grant as a favor to

induō, -ere, induī, indūtum, to put on (a piece of clothing)

ineō, -īre, inīvī/iniī, initum, to go into; **cōnsilium inīre,** to form a plan

īnfimus, -a, -um, *adj.,* lowest

īnfīnītus, -a, -um, *adj.,* boundless, unlimited, infinite, immense* C14

īnflīgō, -ere, īnflīxī, īnflīctum, to strike on or against, inflict* C15

ingēns, ingentis, *adj.,* huge* C4

ingrātus, -a, -um, *adj.,* unwelcome, unpleasant

ingredior, ingredī, ingressus sum, to enter

inimīcitia, -ae, *f.,* hostility

inimīcus, -ī, *m.,* enemy, opponent* A2

inīquitās, -ātis, *f.,* injustice*

initium, -ī, *n.,* beginning*

iniūria, -ae, *f.,* unjust treatment, injury* A3

innītor, innītī, innīxus/innīsus sum, to lean on

inopia, -ae, *f.,* want, helplessness, scarcity, poverty* C6

inquam, I say/I said (*only introducing direct speech*)*

inquiētus, -a, -um, *adj.,* restless, unquiet

inquit, s/he says or said (*only introducing direct speech*)*

inquiunt (plural of *inquit*), they say (*only introducing direct speech*)* C12

īnsequor, īnsequī, īnsecūtus sum, to pursue (in a hostile manner)

īnstituō, -ere, īnstituī, īnstitūtum, + *acc.* + *abl.,* to train or educate someone in some skill

īnstitūtum, -ī, *n.,* way, manner

īnsula, -ae, *f.,* island* C1

Īnsulae Fortūnātae, -ārum, *f. pl.,* Canary Islands

intellegō, -ere, intellēxī, intellēctum, to understand*

inter, *prep.* + *acc.,* between, among*

intercēdō, -ere, intercessī, intercessum, to go between, intervene

interdum, *adv.,* sometimes* C2

interfector, interfectōris, *m.,* slayer, assassin

interficiō, -ere, interfēcī, interfectum, to kill

interpellō (1), to interrupt

interpōnō, -ere, interposuī, interpositum, to put between; **sē interpōnere,** to interfere, intervene

interpretor, interpretārī, interpretātus sum, to interpret

intersum, interesse, interfuī, —, + *dat.,* to get involved in, participate in

intimē, *adv.,* as a close friend, on intimate terms

intimus, -a, -um, *adj.,* most intimate, closest* A1

intrīnsecus, *adv.,* on the inside

intrō (1), to enter*

invādō, -ere, invāsī, —, to burst in* C4

inveniō, -īre, invēnī, inventum, to come upon, find* C1

investīgō (1), to investigate, search into

invideō, -ēre, invīdī, invīsum, + *dat.,* to envy someone*

invītō (1), to invite

invītus, -a, -um, *adj.,* unwilling

iocor, iocārī, iocātus sum, to joke

iocus, -ī, *m.,* joke* C5

ipse, ipsa, ipsum, *demonstrative pronoun and adj.,* -self* C13

īra, -ae, *f.,* anger*

īrāscor, īrāscī, īrātus sum, to be angry* C13

is, ea, id, *personal and demonstrative pronoun and adj.,* s/he, it, this*

iste, ista, istud, *demonstrative pronoun and adj.,* that (of yours)* C13

ita, *adv.,* so, in such a way; yes*

Italia, -ae, *f.,* Italy* A2

itaque, *conj.,* and so*

item, *adv.,* likewise

iter, itineris, *n.,* road, trip* C9

iterum, *adv.,* again* C15

iubeō, -ēre, iussī, iussum, + *acc.* + *inf.,* to order somebody to do something*

iūcundus, -a, -um, *adj.,* pleasant, agreeable, delightful* C10

iūdex, -icis, *m.,* judge*

iūdicium, -ī, *n.,* court, court case; **iūdicium . . . habēre,** to be involved in a court case

iūdicō (1), to judge*

iungō, -ere, iūnxī, iūnctum, to join* C3

iūs, iūris, *n.,* law, right; **in iūs īre,** to go to court, take legal action

iussus, -ūs, *m.,* order (usually employed in the ablative singular only)*

iūstus, -a, -um, *adj.,* legitimate, just*

iuventūs, -ūtis, *f.,* youth* C5

iūvō, -āre, iūvī, iūtum, to help

L

L., the abbreviation for the praenomen Lūcius

L. Lūcullus, -ī, *m.,* a powerful Roman general and politician in the first century BCE

lābor, lābī, lāpsus sum, to slide, slip, glide down* C9

labor, -ōris, *m.,* labor, toil* C10

lacrima, -ae, *f.,* tear*

laedō, -ere, laesī, laesum, to harm* C10

lāmentum, -ī, *n.,* lament, complaint

largītiō, largītiōnis, *f.,* prodigality, lavish expenditure, corruption

Latīnē, *adv.,* in Latin* C8

Latīnus, -a, -um, *adj.,* Latin, pertaining to Latin* C8

lātus, -a, -um, *adj.,* broad, wide

latus, lateris, *n.,* side, flank; **latus fodere,** to stab someone's side with an elbow

laudō (1), to praise* C6

laus, laudis, *f.,* praise

lēctiō, -ōnis, *f.,* reading

lēgātus, -ī, *m.,* ambassador* C11

legō, -ere, lēgī, lēctum, to read, choose*

lepor, lepōris, *m.,* charm, agreeableness

levis, -e, *adj.,* light, trivial* C5

levō (1), lighten, relieve

lēx, lēgis, *f.,* law*

līber, lībera, līberum, *adj.,* free* C10

liber, librī, *m.,* book*

līberālis, -e, *adj.,* befitting a free man, generous; **artēs līberālēs,** the liberal arts (typically grammar, rhetoric, and dialectic)

līberālitās, -ātis, *f.,* generosity* A3

līberī, -ōrum, *m. pl.,* children

līberō (1), + *acc.* + *abl.,* to free someone from something*

lībertās, -ātis, *f.,* freedom* C7

librārius, -ī, *m.,* a slave trained in copying, copyist, secretary

licet, + *dat.* + *inf.,* it is allowed, it is permitted for someone to do something*

ligneus, -a, -um, *adj.,* made of wood* C4

ligō (1), to tie

lingua, -ae, *f.,* language, tongue (*as physical part of the mouth*)* C8

līs, lītis, *f.,* dispute, quarrel* C2

littera, -ae, *f.,* letter of the alphabet; **litterae, -ārum,** *f. pl.,* literature, letter (epistle)*

litterātus, -a, -um, *adj.,* versed in literature, cultured* A5

lītus, -oris, *n.,* shore*

locus, -ī, *m.,* place; **locī, -ōrum,** *m. pl.,* passages of a book; **loca, -ōrum,** *n. pl.,* geographical places*

longē, *adv.,* far*

longus, -a, -um, *adj.,* long*

loquor, loquī, locūtus sum, to speak* C8

lūcidus, -a, -um, *adj.,* bright

lūcrum, -ī, *n.,* profit, gain* C10

lūdō, -ere, lūsī, lūsum, to play*

lūmen, -inis, *n.,* light* C7

lupa, -ae, *f.,* she-wolf*

M

M. = Mārcus, Roman first name

M. Brūtus, -ī, *m.,* Marcus Brutus

magis, *adv.,* more* C8

magister, magistrī, *m.,* teacher (male)* C3

magistrātus, -ūs, *m.,* office of a magistrate, magistracy* A8

magnī habeō, esteem a lot* C11

magnificus, -a, -um, *adj.,* magnificent

magnus, -a, -um, *adj.,* large, great, important*

maior, maius, *adj. comparative,* greater* C8

maiōrēs, maiōrum, *m. pl.,* ancestors

mālō, mālle, māluī, —, to prefer* C7

malus, -a, -um, *adj.,* bad*

mandō (1), to assign, order

māne, *adv.,* in the morning* C2

maneō, -ēre, mānsī, mānsum, to remain*

mantica, -ae, *f.,* briefcase, travel bag

manus, -ūs, *f.,* hand*

Mārcus Tullius Cicero, -ōnis, *m.,* Marcus Tullius Cicero

mare, maris, *n.,* sea*

margarīta, -ae, *f.,* pearl

maritimus, -a, -um, maritime, belonging to the sea, near the sea* C10

marītus, -ī, *m.,* husband*

Marius, -ī, *m.,* civil war leader against Sulla

Martīnus (-ī) Alfonsus (-ī) Pinzon (indeclinable), *m.,* Martín Alfonso Pinzón

māter, mātris, *f.,* mother*

māteria, -ae, *f.,* material

mātrimōnium, -ī, *n.,* marriage* C3

matūrē, *adv.,* early

maximē, *adv. superlative,* most* C14

maximus, -a, -um, *adj. superlative,* greatest* C8

mēcum = cum mē, with me*

medicīna, -ae, *f.,* medicine

medicus, -ī, *m.,* doctor

mediocris, -e, *adj.,* commonplace, mediocre, moderate* A5

medium, -ī, *n.,* the middle, midst* C14

medius, -a, -um, *adj.,* middle* C14

melior, melius, *adj. comparative,* better* C8

meminī, meminisse, to remember* A3

memor, -oris, *adj.* + *gen.,* remembering, mindful of (*usually of one's obligations*)* A1

memoria, -ae, *f.,* memory*

mendācium, -ī, *n.,* lie* A6

mēns, mentis, *f.,* mind, spirit* C5

mentiō, -ōnis, *f.,* mention

mereor, merērī, meritus sum, to deserve

merīdiānus, -a, -um, *adj.,* southern

merīdiēs, -ēī, *m.,* midday, south* C1

meritō, *adv.,* deservedly

metallum, -ī, *n.,* metal

meus, -a, -um, *possessive adj.,* my*

migrō (1), to move from one place to another

mīles, -itis, *m.,* soldier*

Minerva, -ae, *f.,* goddess of wisdom and war (in Greek her name is Athena)

minimē, *adv. superlative,* least, very little; no* C11

minimus, -a, -um, *adj. superlative,* smallest, least* C8

minor, minus, *adj. comparative,* smaller* C8

minuō, -ere, minuī, minūtum, to diminish

minus, *adv. comparative,* less* C8

mīror, -ārī, -ātus sum, to marvel, be surprised at* C13

miser, misera, miserum, *adj.,* wretched*

mittō, -ere, mīsī, missum, to send*

mōbilitās, -ātis, *f.,* mobility

moderor, moderārī, moderātus sum, to manage, direct, guide* C9

modo, *adv.,* only

modo . . . modo . . ., at one time . . . at another . . ., now . . . now . . . * A2

modus, -ī, *m.,* way, method, manner* C10

molestus, -a, -um, *adj.,* troublesome

monastērium, -ī, *n.,* monastery

monīle, monīlis, *n.,* necklace

mōns, montis, *m.,* mountain*

mōnstrum, -ī, *n.,* monster

morbus, -ī, *m.,* illness, sickness* A10

mōre maiōrum, in accord with the custom of <our> ancestors

moriēns, morientis, *adj.*, dying

mōriō, -ōnis, *m.*, fool, clown

morior, morī, mortuus sum, to die* C12

moror, morārī, morātus sum, to stay for a long or short period, spend time* A9

mors, mortis, *f.*, death*

mōs, mōris, *m.*, custom, habit; *pl.*, morals* C1

mōtus, -ūs, *m.*, motion, movement* C14

moveō, -ēre, mōvī, mōtum, to move*

mox, *adv.*, soon*

mulier, -ieris, *f.*, woman*

multitūdō, -ūdinis, *f.*, crowd, throng* C13

multō, *adv.*, by much* C14

multum, *adv.*, much*

multus, -a, -um, *adj.*, much, many*; **multum** + *partitive gen.*, a lot of

munditia, -ae, *f.*, neatness, cleanliness

mundus, -ī, *m.*, world* C1

mūnus, mūneris, *n.*, gift

mūrus, -ī, *m.*, wall, wall-fence*

mūtātiō, -ōnis, *f.*, change

Mutina, -ae, *f.*, Mutina, city in northern Italy, called Modena today

mūtō (1), to change*

N

nam, *conj.*, for, in fact*

namque, *conj.*, indeed, for, because* A6

nancīscor, nancīscī, nactus/nanctus sum, to gain possession of, acquire

nārrō (1), to tell*

nāscor, nāscī, nātus sum, to be born* A9

Nāsō, -ōnis, *m.*, Ovid

nātiō, -ōnis, *f.*, a race of people, tribe

nātīvus, -a, -um, *adj.*, inborn, native

natō (1), to swim

nātū maxima/minima, oldest/youngest

nātūra, -ae, *f.*, nature, character* C14

nātūrālis, nātūrāle, *adj.*, natural

nātūrāliter, *adv.*, naturally

nātus, -a, -um, *adj.*, born

nauta, -ae, *m.*, sailor*

nāvigātiō, -ōnis, *f.*, sea voyage

nāvigō (1), to sail, voyage*

nāvis, -is, *f.*, ship*

nē . . . quidem . . ., not even* A5

-ne, a particle added to the first word of an interrogative sentence*

nē, *conj.* + *subjunctive*, in order not to, lest, that not, not to* C3

nebulō, -ōnis, *m.*, a worthless fellow

nec, *conj.*, and not, nor; **nec . . . nec . . .,** neither . . . nor . . . * C4

necdum, *adv.*, *conj.*, and not yet

necessāriō, *adv.*, necessarily* C14

necessārius, -a, -um, *adj.* necessary* A3

necesse est, it is necessary; + *dat.* + *inf.*, it is necessary for someone to do something* C6

necessitūdō, -ūdinis, *f.*, bond* A9

nefās (indeclinable), *n.*, a crime, a sacrilege

neglegō, -ere, neglēxī, neglēctum, to neglect*

negō (1), to deny* C13

nēmō, *m.*, no one* C6

nēmō nōn, everybody

neptis, -is, *f.*, granddaughter

neque = nec, *conj.*, and not; **neque . . . neque . . .,** neither . . . nor . . . * A3

neque eō sētius, nevertheless

neque sōlum . . . sed etiam . . ., not only . . . but also . . .

nesciō, -īre, -īvī, -ītum, not to know* C11

neuter, neutra, neutrum, *adj.*, neither, none of two* C11

nihil, *adv.*, in no way, not at all

nihil, *negative pronoun*, nothing*

nihilō sētius, nonetheless, just the same

nihilōminus, *conj.*, nevertheless

nimis, *adj.*, too much* C12

nisi, *conj.*, if not, unless* C12

nītor, nītī, nīsus/nīxus sum, to strive to achieve* A6

nix, nivis, *f.*, snow* C9

nōbilis, nōbile, *adj.*, noble, distinguished

noctū, *adv.*, during the night*

nōlō, nōlle, nōluī, —, not to want, be unwilling* C7

nōmen, -inis, *n.*, name*

Nōmentānus, -a, -um, *adj.*, belonging to Nomentum, a town in Latium

nōn, *negative adv.*, not*

nōn sōlum . . ., sed etiam . . ., not only . . ., but also . . . *

nōnnūllī, -ae, -a, *adj.*, a good number, quite a few, some

nōs, *personal pronoun*, we*

noster, nostra, nostrum, *possessive adj.*, our*

notō (1), to indicate, note

novus, -a, -um, *adj.*, new*

nox, noctis, *f.*, night*

nūbēs, -is, *f.*, cloud*

nūbō, -ere, nūpsī, nūptum + *dat.*, to marry (*used for a woman marrying a man*)

nūllus, -a, -um, *adj.*, none* C11

numerō (1), to number, count among* C13

numerus, -ī, *m.*, number* A2

numquam, *adv.*, never*

nunc, *adv.*, now*

nūptiae, -ārum, *f. pl.*, wedding, marriage* A4

nusquam, *adv.*, nowhere* C3

O

ō, *interj.*, oh!

oblīvīscor, oblīvīscī, oblītus sum, + *gen.*, to forget* A3

obsecrō (1), to beseech, entreat

observantia, -ae, *f.*, regard

obstinātiō, -ōnis, *f.*, obstinacy, stubbornness

obtineō, -ēre, obtinuī, obtentum, to hold, hold onto

obtrectātiō, obtrectātiōnis, *f.*, an envious detracting, disparaging

occidēns, occidentis, *m.*, west

occīdō, -ere, occīdī, occīsum, to kill*

occultō (1), to hide*

occupātiō, -ōnis, *f.*, preoccupation with business, engagement

occupō (1), to occupy* C1

ōceanus, -ī, *m.*, ocean

oculus, -ī, *m.*, eye*

odium, -ī, *n.*, hatred; **odiō habeō,** + *acc.*, I hate somebody* C2

offendō, -ere, offendī, offēnsum, to happen upon, offend* C13

offēnsiō, offēnsiōnis, *f.*, offense, cause for offense

officium, -ī, *n.*, favor, duty, sense of duty, service, kindness* C12

olea, -ae, *f.,* olive

ōlim, *adv.,* once upon a time

omnīnō, *adv.,* wholly, entirely

omnis, -e, *adj.,* each, every, all*

onus, oneris, *n.,* weight, burden* C9

operae pretium est, it is worthwhile* C11

operam dō + *dat.,* to give care to

opīniō, opīniōnis, *f.,* opinion, mind* A1

oppidum, -ī, *n.,* town* C15

opprimō, -ere, oppressī, oppressum, to overwhelm, suppress*

ops, opis, *f.,* aid, wealth; **opēs, opium,** *f. pl.,* resources, money

optimus, -a, -um, *adj.,* best* C8

opus est, is necessary

ōrāculum, -ī, *n.,* oracle*

ōrātiō, -ōnis, *f.,* speech; **ōrātiōnem habeō,** to make a speech*

orbis, orbis, *m.,* circle, disc, globe; **orbis terrārum,** the earth, the world* C12

ōrdinō (1), to place in order

ōrdō, ōrdinis, *m.,* order, social class, class (in society)* A9

orīgō, orīginis, *f.,* origin* A8

orior, orīrī, ortus sum + *abl.,* to be born of, be descended from, originate* A9

ōrnāmentum, -ī, *n.,* ornament, distinction

ōrnātus, -a, -um, *adj.,* adorned* C7

ornātus, -ūs, *m.,* apparel, attire

ōrō (1), to ask, entreat* C5

ortus, -ūs, *m.,* raising, beginning, origin; **ortus sōlis,** east* C1

ōs, ōris, *n.,* mouth*

ōsculor, ōsculārī, ōsculātus sum, to kiss

ostendō, -ere, ostendī, ostentum, to show*

ostrea, -ae, *f.,* oyster

ōtium, -ī, *n.,* leisure, free time* C7

P

P. = Pūblius

paene, *adv.,* almost*

palam, *adv.,* openly

Pannonia, -ae, *f.,* a region which approximately corresponds to modern Hungary

pār, paris, *adj.,* equal* A5

parcō, -ere, pepercī, —, + *dat.,* to spare somebody or something* C4

parēns, -rentis, *m./f.,* parent*

pariō, -ere, peperī, partum, to give birth to* C3

parō (1), to prepare, get ready, design*

pars, partis, *f.,* part*

partior, partīrī, partītus sum, to divide, distribute* C8

parvus, -a, -um, *adj.,* small*

passer, -eris, *m.,* sparrow*

pateō, -ēre, patuī, —, to be open, be available

pater, patris, *m.,* father*

patior, patī, passus sum, to endure, tolerate, suffer, allow* C8

patria, -ae, *f.,* fatherland*

paucī, -ae, -a, *adj.,* few*

paulisper, *adv.,* for a little while* C10

paulō, *adv.,* a little bit, to a small extent* C6

pauper, pauperis, *adj.,* poor*

pāx, pācis, *f.,* peace*

pectus, -oris, *n.,* chest*

pecūnia, -ae, *f.,* money* C10

pecūniōsus, -a, -um, *adj.,* moneyed, provided with money

pedisequus, -ī, *m.,* manservant

peior, peius, *adj. comparative,* worse* C8

pellis, -is, *f.,* skin, hide*

pendeō, -ēre, pependī, —, to hang (intransitive)

penes, *prep.* + *acc.,* in the possession of

per, *prep.* + *acc.,* through*

peragō, -ere, perēgī, perāctum, to carry out, perform

percipiō, -ere, percēpī, perceptum, to take, earn, acquire* A3

percutiō, -ere, percussī, percussum, to strike through* C15

perdō, -ere, perdidī, perditum, to lose, waste* C3

peregrīnātiō, peregrīnātiōnis, *f.,* journeying

perīculum, -ī, *n.,* danger*

perpendiculāris, -e, *adj.,* perpendicular

perpendō, -ere, perpendī, perpēnsum, to ponder, weigh carefully

perperam, *adv.,* wrongly, incorrectly* C14

perpetuō, *adv.,* without interruption

perpetuus, -a, -um, *adj.,* continuous, permanent

perscrībō, -ere, perscrīpsī, perscrīptum, to write a detailed account of

persequor, persequī, persecūtus sum, to follow persistently, go over

persuādeō, -ēre, persuāsī, persuāsum, to persuade

pertineō, -ēre, pertinuī, pertentum, to relate to, pertain to

perturbō (1), to throw into confusion

perveniō, -īre, -vēnī, -ventum, to arrive* C9

pessimus, -a, -um, *adj. superlative,* worst* C8

petō, -ere, petīvī, petītum, to seek, head for, go to, rush to*

philosophus, -ī, *m.,* philosopher

Pictus, -ī, *m.,* a Pict

pietās, pietātis, *f.,* sense of duty, dutifulness to family and society

pilleus, -ī, *m.,* hat

piscis, -is, *m.,* fish* C1

placeō, -ēre, placuī, placitum, + *dat.,* to please, be agreeable to somebody* C5

placidus, -a, -um, *adj.,* peaceful, calm* C10

plācō (1), to placate, soothe

planēta, -ae, *m.,* planet

plēnus, -a, -um, *adj.* + *gen.* or + *abl.,* full of*

pluit, -ere, pluit, —, *an impersonal verb (used only in 3rd sg.),* to rain

plumbum, -ī, *n.,* lead

plūrēs, plūra, *adj. comparative,* more* C8

plūrimus, -a, -um, *adj. superlative,* most* C8

plūs, *adv.,* more

plūs, plūris, *adj. comparative,* + *partitive gen.,* more* C8

pluvia, -ae, *f.,* rain

poēma, poēmatis, *n.,* poem

poēta, -ae, *m.,* poet*

poēticē, poēticēs (poēticēn), *f.,* poetry

poēticus, -a, -um, *adj.,* poetic

polliceor, pollicērī, pollicitus sum, to promise* A6

Pompēius, -ī, *m.,* Pompey

Pompōnius, -ī, *m.,* the first name of Atticus

pōmum, -ī, *n.,* fruit*

ponderōsus, -a, -um, *adj.,* heavy

pondus, -eris, *n.,* weight* C14

pōnō, -ere, posuī, positum, to put, place*

pōns, pontis, *m.,* bridge* C4

populus, -ī, *m.,* people* C11

porta, -ae, *f.,* gate* C4

pōscō, -ere, popōscī, —, to demand

possessiō, -ōnis, *f.,* possession

possideō, -ēre, possēdī, possessum, to possess*

possum, posse, potuī, —, to be able, can*

post, *prep. + acc.,* after*

posteā, *adv.,* afterward*

posteāquam = postquam

posterī, -ōrum, *m. pl.,* descendants, coming generations

postquam, *conj.,* after*

potēns, potentis, *adj.,* powerful* C7

potentia, -ae, *f.,* power* A4

potestās, -ātis, *f.,* command, control, power* A4

potior, potīrī, potītus sum, + *gen.,* to make oneself master of, take possession of

potissimum, *adv.,* especially, above all

potius, *adv.,* rather* C10

praebeō, -ēre, praebuī, praebitum, to offer, give

praecipuē, *adv.,* particularly, especially* A7

praecipuus, -a, -um, *adj.,* peculiar, special, exceptional

praeclārus, -a, -um, *adj.,* famous, distinguished, excellent, renowned*

praedicō (1), to proclaim

praedīcō, -ere, praedīxī, praedictum, to predict

praeditus, -a, -um, + *abl.,* endowed with, possessed of* C15

praedium, -ī, *n.,* estate, land

praefātiō, -ōnis, *f.,* preface

praefectūra, -ae, *f.,* an office in governing a province

praemium, -ī, *n.,* reward, prize*

praeoptō (1), + *acc.* + *dat.,* to prefer something to something

praesertim, *adv.,* especially* C14

praesidium, -ī, *n.,* military escort, garrison* A2

praestō, -āre, praestitī, praestitum, to make available, supply; fulfill, perform, offer; surpass, exceed, excel* A1

praestringō, -ere, praestrīnxī, praestrictum, to bind fast, to strike; **oculōs praestringere,** to blind

praeter, *prep. + acc.,* except, besides, in addition to, beyond * A6

praetermittō, -ere, praetermīsī, praetermissum, to allow to go, let pass

praetor, praetōris, *m.,* praetor

praetūra, -ae, *f.,* praetorship

prāvus, -a, -um, *adj.,* crooked, bad

prex, precis, *f.,* prayer* A10

prīdem, *adv.,* long ago

prīmā nocte, on the first night

prīmō, *adv.,* at first* C4

prīmum, *adv.,* first* C10

prīmus, -a, -um, *adj.,* first*

prīnceps, prīncipis, *adj.,* distinguished, first

prīnceps, prīncipis, *m.,* leading citizen, leader, chief* A7

prīncipātus, prīncipātūs, *m.,* first place

prīvātus, -a, -um, *adj.,* private, apart from the public sphere

prīvātus, -ī, *m.,* private citizen

prīvignus, -ī, *m.,* stepson

prō, *prep. + abl.,* for, on behalf of*

prō certō, *adverbial phrase,* for certain, for sure*

probābilis, -e, *adj.,* probable

probō (1), to approve* C12

prōcēdō, -ere, prōcessī, prōcessum, to advance, proceed

procella, -ae, *f.,* violent storm, gale

procul, *adv.,* far, far away* C1

prōcumbō, -ere, prōcubuī, prōcubitum, to fall forward, prostrate oneself

prōdūcō, -ere, prōdūxī, prōductum, to bring forth, lengthen

proelium, -ī, *n.,* battle, combat*

professiō, -ōnis, *f.,* profession

proficīscor, proficīscī, profectus sum, to set out, depart

profugiō, -ere, profūgī, —, to run away, flee

profundus, -a, -um, *adj.,* deep, profound, bottomless

prōgredior, prōgredī, prōgressus sum, to go forward, proceed* C9

prohibeō, -ēre, prohibuī, prohibitum, to prevent

prōiciō, -ere, prōiēcī, prōiectum, to send forth, (*in passive participle*) protruding

prōmittō, -ere, prōmīsī, prōmissum, to promise* C1

prōnūntiō (1), to pronounce, recite, deliver (of a speech)

prōpāgātiō, -ōnis, *f.,* spreading, propagation

propāgō, propāginis, *f.,* offspring, progeny

prope, *prep. + acc.,* near* C1

prōpōnō, -ere, prōposuī, prōpositum, to propose

prōpositum, -ī, *n.,* intention, proposition

propter, *prep. + acc.,* because of, on account of*

prōscrībō, -ere, prōscrīpsī, prōscrīptum, to proscribe, publish someone's name in a list of outlaws

prōscrīptiō, -ōnis, *f.,* proscription, publishing the names of citizens declared to be outlaws

prosper, prospera, prosperum, *adj.,* fortunate, prosperous* C10

prosperitās, -ātis, *f.,* fortunate state of things, prosperity

prout, *conj.,* as

prōvincia, -ae, *f.,* province (territorial), any duty or sphere of activity (not territorial)

proximus, -a, -um, *adj.,* nearest* C5

prūdēns, prūdentis, *adj.,* prudent

prūdentia, -ae, *f.,* practical intelligence, wisdom, prudence, foreseeing* A2

pūblicē, *adv.,* publicly, on behalf of the state

pūblicus, -a, -um, *adj.,* common, public, belonging to the state; **rēs publica,** state* C7

puella, -ae, *f.,* girl*

puer, puerī, *m.,* boy*

puerīlis, puerīle, *adj.,* related to *puer;* **puerīlis aetās,** boyhood

pueritia, -ae, *f.,* childhood

pugnō (1), to fight*

pulcher, pulchra, pulchrum, *adj.,* beautiful, nice*

pulchrē, *adv.,* beautifully

pūniō, -īre, -īvī, -ītum, to punish*

putō (1), to think, consider*

Q

Q. = Quīntus

Q. Caecilius, -ī, *m.,* Quīntus Caecilius

Q. Cicero, Cicerōnis, *m.,* = Quīntus Cicero

Q. Hortēnsius, -ī, *m.,* Quīntus Hortensius

quaerō, -ere, quaesīvī, quaesītum, to look for, search*

quaestiō, -ōnis, *f.,* question, dispute, investigation

quaestus, -ūs, *m.,* profit

quālis, quāle, *interrogative and relative pronoun,* what sort of* C7

quam, + *superlative degree,* as . . . as possible* A3

quam, *interrogative adv. and exclamation particle,* how* C4

quam, *used with comparative words,* than* C6

quamdiū, *adv. and conj.,* as long as

quamdiū, *interrogative adv.,* for how long* A9

quamquam, *conj.,* although* C12

quamvīs, *conj.,* although* C12

quantum, *interrogative and relative adv.,* as much as, as much; how much, to what extent* C6

quantus, -a, -um, *interrogative and relative adj.,* how much, how great* C4

quārē, *conj.,* therefore, hence* A10

quartus, -a, -um, *adj.,* fourth

quaternī, -ae, -a, *adj.,* four each (*a distributive*)

-que, *conj.,* and*

quī, quae, quod, *relative pronoun,* which, who, that*

quī, quae, quod?, *interrogative adjective,* which? what?*

quia, *conj.,* because* C12

quīdam, quaedam, quiddam, *indefinite pronoun;* **quīdam, quaedam, quoddam,** *indefinite adjective,* a certain* A7

quidem, *adv.,* indeed* C12

quiēs, -ētis, *f.,* rest, repose* C14

quīn, *conj.* + *subjunctive,* without its being the case that (*after negative clauses*)* A9

quīn etiam, and furthermore

quīnī, -ae, -a, *adj.,* five each (*a distributive*)

quīnquāgintā, numeral, fifty

quīnque, numeral, five

quīntus, -a, -um, *adj.,* fifth

Quīntus (-ī) Tullius (-ī) Cicero (Cicerōnis), *m.,* Quīntus Tullius Cicero

Quīntus (-ī) Hortēnsius (-ī), *m.,* a famous orator

Quirītēs, -ium, *m. pl.,* Roman citizens

quis, quid?, *interrogative pronoun,* who? what?*

quisquam, quicquam (quidquam), *indefinite pronoun (mainly in negative sentences),* any, anybody* A9

quisquis, quidquid (quicquid), *indefinite pronoun,* whoever, whatever

quōcum = cum quō

quod, *conj.,* because, the fact that* C12

quōdam diē, a certain day, one day

quōmodo, *adv.,* how* C11

quōquam, *adv.,* to any place

quoque, *adv.,* also*

quotiēs, *conj.,* as often as* C9

quoūsque, *adv.,* how far, to what extent

R

rāmus, -ī, *m.,* branch

rapiō, -ere, rapuī, raptum, to snatch

recipiō, -ere, recēpī, receptum, to receive, take back; **mē recipiō,** I retreat* C4

rēctē, *adv.,* correctly

reddō, -ere, reddidī, redditum, to render, make, give back* C10

redeō, -īre, -īvī, -itum, to go back, return* C13

redūcō, -ere, redūxī, reductum, to lead back

referō, referre, rettulī, relātum, to carry back, report* C13

rēgia, -ae, *f.,* royal palace

rēgīna, -ae, *f.,* queen*

rēgnō (1), to reign, rule

religiōsē, *adv.,* scrupulously, conscientiously

relinquō, -ere, relīquī, relictum, to leave behind, abandon*

reliquus, -a, -um, *adj.,* the rest of, the remaining; **reliquum facere,** to leave over* A10

rēmaneō, -ēre, rēmānsī, rēmānsum, to remain

remigrō (1), to go back, return

removeō, -ēre, remōvī, remōtum, to move back, remove

repellō, -ere, reppulī, repulsum, to push back, thrust back* C15

repraesentō (1), to represent

reprehendō, -ere, -prehendī, -prehēnsum, to blame, rebuke*

requīrō, -ere, requīsīvī, requīsītum, to try to find, inquire about

rēs, reī, *f.,* thing, matter*

rēs familiāris (familiāris, familiāre), family resources, wealth, personal property, family estate, estate

rēs (rērum) gestae, -ārum, *f. pl.,* deeds, exploits, things done, history, past actions* A8

reservō (1), to keep, reserve

resistō, -ere, restitī, —, to resist, oppose; + *dat.,* to resist (*somebody or something*)* C4

respondeō, -ēre, -spondī, -spōnsum, to answer*

restituō, -ere, restituī, restitūtum, to restore* C6

retineō, -ēre, retinuī, retentum, to retain, keep

reverenter, *adv.,* respectfully

revolūtiō, -ōnis, *f.,* revolving

rēx, rēgis, *m.,* king*

rīdeō, -ēre, rīsī, rīsum, to laugh* C15

rīvus, -ī, *m.,* brook, stream*

rixa, -ae, *f.,* quarrel

rogō (1), to ask*

Rōma, -ae, *f.,* Rome*

Rōmānus, -a, -um, *adj.,* Roman*

rota, -ae, *f.,* wheel*

ruber, rubra, rubrum, *adj.,* red*

rumpō, -ere, rūpī, ruptum, to break, tear* C15

rūs, rūris, *n.,* countryside

rūsticus, -a, -um, *adj.,* rural, rustic*

S

sacer, sacra, sacrum, *adj.,* sacred

saepe, *adv.,* often*

sāl, salis, *m.,* salt, a quality that gives taste, wit* A5

saliō, -īre, saluī, saltum, to jump

salūs, -ūtis, *f.,* health, welfare; **salūtem dīcō,** + *dat.,* I greet (a customary way to begin a letter)* C3

salūtō (1), to greet* C11

sanciō, -īre, sānxī, sānctum, to ratify solemnly, confirm* A9

Sanctus (-ī) Stephanus (-ī), *m.,* St. Stephen

sanguis, -inis, *m.,* blood*

sānō (1), to heal*

sapientia, -ae, *f.,* wisdom

sarcina, -ae, *f.* (*used mostly in pl.*), burden, baggage* C10

satelles, satellitis, *m.,* satellite

satis, *adv.,* enough, sufficiently* C6

satisfaciō, -ere, satisfēcī, satisfactum, to give satisfaction, give all that is required (*often with dat.*)

saxum, -ī, *n.,* stone, rock*

scandō, -ere, —, —, to climb over, mount

scelestus, -a, -um, *adj.,* wicked* C10

scindō, -ere, scindī, scissum, to tear, cut

sciō, -īre, -īvī, -ītum, to know*

scopulōsus, -a, -um, *adj.,* full of shoals, rocky

Scōttus, -ī, *m.,* a Scot

scrībō, -ere, scrīpsī, scrīptum, to write* C3

Scythia, -ae, *f.,* Scythia (a territory in southern Russia today)

s.d. = salūtem dīcit

sē, *acc. of the reflexive pronoun,* herself, himself, itself, themselves*

sēcum = cum sē

secundus, -a, -um, *adj.,* favorable, second* C6

sed, *conj.,* but*

sedeō, -ēre, sēdī, sessum, to sit*

sēdēs, -is, *f.,* seat, abode* C15

semel, *adv.,* once* C10

semper, *adv.,* always*

senectūs, -ūtis, *f.,* old age*

senēscō, -ere, senuī, —, to get old, grow old

senex, -is, *m.,* old man*

sententia, -ae, *f.,* opinion, point of view* C12

sentiō, -īre, sēnsī, sēnsum, to feel*

sēparō (1), to separate*

septem, *numeral,* seven

septentriōnālis, -e, *adj.,* northern* C1

septuāgintā, *numeral,* seventy

sequor, sequī, secūtus sum, to follow* C8

serēnus, -a, -um, *adj.,* calm, clear* C10

sēriō, *adv.,* seriously

sermō, sermōnis, *m.,* conversation, speech

serviō, -īre, servīvī, servītum, to be of service, comply with

servitūs, -ūtis, *f.,* slavery

servō (1), to save, preserve*

servus, -ī, *m.,* slave, servant* C11

sestertius, -ī, *m.,* sesterce, Roman silver coin

sevēritās, -ātis, *f.,* sternness, severity

sevērus, -a, -um, *adj.,* serious, strict, severe*

sexāgintā, *numeral,* sixty

sī, *conj.,* if*

sibi, *dat. of the reflexive pronoun,* to himself/herself/itself/themselves*

sīc, *adv.,* in such a way, in this way, so* C15

sīcut, *adv.,* just as, just in the same way*

sīdus, -eris, *n.,* constellation* C15

signum, -ī, *n.,* sign

silva, -ae, *f.,* forest*

similis, -e, *adj.* + *gen.* or + *dat.,* like, similar*

similitūdō, similitūdinis, *f.,* similarity

simplex, simplicis, *adj.,* simple

simul, *adv.,* at the same time, simultaneously* C4

simul ac, *conj.,* as soon as* C9

simultās, -ātis, *f.,* rivalry

sine, *prep.* + *abl.,* without*

singulāris, -e, *adj.,* unique, exceptional, special, unparalleled

singulī, -ae, -a, *adj.,* one apiece, one each (*a distributive*)* A8

sinō, -ere, sīvī, situm, + *acc.* + *inf.,* to allow somebody to do something* C2

Siōn, Siōnis, *m./f.,* a hill in Jerusalem

situs, -a, -um, *adj.,* situated, located* C1

socius, -ī, *m.,* associate, partner, ally* C13

sōl, sōlis, *m.,* sun* C1

soleō, -ēre, solitus sum, —, + *inf.,* to be accustomed*

sōlus, -a, -um, *adj.,* alone*

somnus, -ī, *m.,* sleep*

sōpiō, -īre, sōpīvī, sōpītum, to lull to sleep, settle

soror, -ōris, *f.,* sister*

sors, sortis, *f.,* lot (in the literal sense of a lot one draws), fate (in the metaphorical sense of one's condition in life)* C12

specimen, speciminis, *n.,* mark, example, proof

spectō (1), to watch* C11

spēlunca, -ae, *f.,* cave*

spērō (1), to hope* C12

spēs, speī, *f.,* hope* C12

splendidus, -a, -um, *adj.,* illustrious, distinguished, shining

splendor, -ōris, *m.,* brilliance, splendor

spoliō (1), + *abl.,* to strip of

spōnsālia, -ium, *n. pl.,* the act or the ceremony of betrothal

spōnsor, -ōris, *m.,* guarantor, one who formally guarantees the good faith of another

stabilis, -e, *adj.,* steady, stable

statim, *adv.,* immediately*

status, -ūs, *m.,* condition, state, attitude

stipulātiō, -ōnis, *f.,* demanding of a guarantee from a prospective debtor

stirps, stirpis, *f.,* stock, descent, race

stō, -āre, stetī, statum, to stand*

strīdor, -ōris, *m.,* a harsh, shrill, or hissing sound

studeō, -ēre, studuī, —, + *dat.,* to study, be eager for, be interested in*

studiōsus, -a, -um, *adj.,* + *gen.,* fond of, interested in* C7

studium, -ī, *n.,* pursuit, activity to which one is devoted, zeal, eagerness* A7

suāvitās, -ātis, *f.,* sweetness, charm, pleasantness* A8

sub, *prep.* + *abl.,* under* A8

subitō, *adv.,* suddenly*

sublevō (1), to support, to help

subterrāneus, -a, -um, *adj.,* underground

subtexō, -ere, subtexuī, subtextum, to add as a supplement

suburbānus, -a, -um, *adj.,* situated near Rome

succurrō, -ere, succurrī, succursum, to hasten to help

suī, sibi, sē, *reflexive pronoun,* herself, himself, itself, themselves*

Sulla, -ae, *m.,* Sulla

Sullānus, -a, -um, *adj.,* related to **Sulla, -ae,** *m.*

sum, esse, fuī, —, to be*

summa, -ae, *f.,* high point, sum total; **summa imperiī,** pinnacle of power

summus, -a, -um, *adj.,* extreme, highest, utmost, supreme, at the top of* A2

sūmō, -ere, sūmpsī, sūmptum, to take* A10

sūmptuōsus, -a, -um, *adj.,* costly, sumptuous

sūmptus, -ūs, *m.,* expense* A5

superior, superiōris, *adj.,* more powerful

superō (1), to surpass, conquer

supersum, superesse, superfuī, —, + *dat.,* to survive something

suprā, *adv.,* beyond, in addition

suspiciō, suspiciōnis, *f.,* suspicion

suus, -a, -um, *possessive adj.,* his, her, its, their*

T

taberna, -ae, *f.,* wineshop

taceō, -ēre, tacuī, tacitum, to be silent, keep quiet* C11

taciturnus, -a, -um, *adj.,* silent

tālis, tāle, *adj.,* such, such a* C13

tam, *adv.,* so*

tam . . . quam . . . , so . . . as . . . * C5

tamdiū . . . quoad . . . , as long . . . as . . .

tamen, *conj.,* however*; nevertheless* C12

Tamphiliānus, -a, -um, made by the architect Tamphilus

tamquam, *adv.,* as* C7

Tancrēdus Normannus, Tancred of Hauteville; along with Bohemond of Taranto, led a powerful contingent of Normans in the First Crusade

tandem, *adv.,* at last*

tangō, -ere, tetigī, tāctum, to touch*

tantopere, *adv.,* so greatly

tantum, *adv.,* only, so much* A4

tantum . . . quantum . . . , as much . . . as . . .

tantus, -a, -um, *adj.,* so great*

tēctum, -ī, *n.,* roof, house* A5

tēcum = cum tē, with you*

tegō, -ere, tēxī, tēctum, to cover, protect* A1

tēlum, -ī, *n.,* spear, javelin* C15

temerē, *adv.,* hardly, heedlessly, without good cause

temeritās, -ātis, *f.,* rashness, recklessness

tēmetipsum, yourself

temperō (1), *ā(b)* + *abl.,* to refrain from

tempestās, -ātis, *f.,* storm*

templum, -ī, *n.,* temple*

temporārius, -a, -um, *adj.,* suited for the occasion, temporary

temporis causā, to suit the occasion

temptō (1), to try*

tempus, -oris, *n.,* circumstance, time*; *pl.,* **tempora,** crisis

tenebrae, -ārum, *f. pl.,* shadows, darkness*

teneō, -ēre, tenuī, tentum, to hold*

tenuis, -e, *adj.,* thin

tergum, -ī, *n.,* back

terō, -ere, trīvī, trītum, to wear out, rub*

terra, -ae, *f.,* land*

terribilis, -e, *adj.,* terrifying*

territus, -a, -um, *adj.,* terrified

terror, -ōris, *m.,* terror

tertius, -a, -um, *adj.,* third* C6

testāmentum, -ī, *n.,* will

testimōnium, -ī, *n.,* testimony* A7

testis, -is, *m.,* witness

Theodosius, -ī, *m.,* Theodosius

Ti. Claudius Nerō, *m.,* Tiberius Claudius Nero, the emperor Claudius

timeō, -ēre, timuī, —, to fear, be afraid*

timor, -ōris, *m.,* fear*

tolerō (1), to tolerate, bear

tollō, -ere, sustulī, sublātum, to lift up, raise, destroy*

tot, *adv.,* so many* C7

tōtus, -a, -um, *adj.,* whole, entire* C11

trādō, -ere, trādidī, trāditum, to give, teach

trahō, -ere, trāxī, trāctum, to drag* C7

trāiciō, -ere, trāiēcī, trāiēctum, to transport, transfer

tranquillitās, tranquillitātis, *f.,* calmness, quiet way of life

tranquillō (1), to make peaceful

tranquillus, -a, -um, *adj.,* quiet, calm

trecenta (HS trecenta mīlia), 300,000 sesterces

trēs, tria, *numeral,* three* C6

tribūnus, -ī, *m.* **plēbī,** tribune of the plebs

tribuō, -ere, tribuī, tribūtum, to grant, bestow, assign, give, attribute* A3

tricēsimus, -a, -um, *adj.,* thirtieth

trīgintā, *numeral,* thirty

trīstis, -e, *adj.,* sad* C6

triumvir, triumvirī, *m.,* member of a committee of three men

tū, *personal pronoun,* you (sg.)*

tueor, -ērī, tuitus/tūtus sum, to look at, protect* A10

tum, *adv.,* then*

tumultus, -ūs, *m.,* uproar, confusion*

tunc, *adv.,* then*

turpis, -e, *adj.,* shameful, disgraceful* C11

turris, -is, *f.,* tower* C13

tūtus, -a, -um, *adj.,* safe* C4

tuus, -a, -um, *possessive adj.,* yours, your (sg.)*

U

ubi?, *interrogative adv.,* where?* C7

ubicumque, *conj.,* wherever; *adv.,* everywhere

ubĭ̄nam, *adv.,* where in the world?

ubīque, *adv.,* everywhere*

ulcīscor, ulcīscī, ultus sum, to take revenge

Ulixēs, -is, *m.,* Odysseus or Ulysses

ūllus, -a, -um, *adj.,* any*

ultimus, -a, -um, *adj.,* last, farthest, most remote

umquam, *adv.,* ever*

ūnā, *adv.,* together*

ūndecim, eleven

undique, *adv.,* from all parts, from everywhere* C14

ūnicus, -a, -um, *adj.,* only one

ūniversus, -a, -um, *adj.,* all together, all, entire

ūnus, ūna, ūnum, *adj.,* one* C7

urbs, urbis, *f.,* city (usually the city of Rome)*

ūsque, *adv.,* right up; **ūsque ad,** up to* A7

ūsūra, -ae, *f.,* interest (of money), interest paid for the use of money

ūsus, -ūs, *m.,* use; **ūsū venīre,** to occur* A7

ut, *conj., + indicative,* as, when, according to; + *perfect indicative,* as soon as, when; + *subjunctive,* in order to, so that, that* C2

uter, utra, utrum, *interrogative adj.,* who?, which (of two)?

uterque, utraque, utrumque, *adj. or pronoun,* each of the two

ūtilis, -e, *adj.,* useful* C7

ūtilitās, -ātis, *f.,* usefulness

utinam, I wish that, if only (a particle of wishing)* C1

Ūtopia, -ae, *f.,* Utopia (in Greek "No Place")

Ūtopiēnsis, Ūtopiēnsis, *m.,* Utopian

ūtor, ūtī, ūsus sum, + *abl.,* to use somebody or something; enjoy the friendship of, avail oneself of* C11

utrum . . . an . . . (introducing a disjunctive question), whether . . . or . . .* A6

uxor, -ōris, *f.,* wife; **uxōrem dūcō,** to marry (a woman)* C3

V

vacātiō, vacātiōnis, *f.,* freedom, exemption from military service

vacuus, -a, -um, + *abl.,* empty of* C4

vadimōnium, -ī, *n.,* guarantee that the defendant will appear before the judge

valdē, *adv.,* very, exceedingly*

valē!, goodbye!*

valēdīcō, -ere, valēdīxī, valēdictum, to say goodbye

valeō, -ēre, valuī, —, + *inf.,* to be able; be in good health; be of value* C2

valētūdō, -ūdinis, *f.,* health* A10

vapor, -ōris, *m.,* steam, vapor

varietās, -ātis, *f.,* variety, diversity, changeable nature

vastus, -a, -um, *adj.,* empty, vast

vātēs, vātis, *m.,* prophet

vector, -ōris, *m.,* passenger

vegetus, -a, -um, *adj.,* lively, vigorous

vehemēns, vehementis, *adj.,* violent, vehement* C5

vehementer, *adv.,* vehemently, strongly* C6

vehō, -ere, vexī, vectum, to drive, carry* C15

vel, *conj.,* or* C2

vel . . . vel . . ., either . . . or . . .

vēlificor, -ārī, vēlificātus sum, to sail

vēlōcitās, -ātis, *f.,* speed, velocity

velut sī, just as if (normally joined with a verb in the subjunctive)

vēnātor, -ōris, *m.,* hunter

vēnditō (1), to try to sell, advertise

venēnum, -ī, *n.,* poison*

venia, -ae, *f.,* pardon, indulgence, forgiveness* C13

veniō, -īre, vēnī, ventum, to come*

venter, -tris, *m.,* stomach, belly

ventitō (1), to go often

ventus, -ī, *m.,* wind*

verbōsus, -a, -um, *adj.,* containing many words, lengthy

verbum, -ī, *n.,* word*

vērē, *adv.,* correctly

vereor, verērī, veritus sum, to fear, respect* C8

vērō, *adv.,* in fact, truly; moreover (introducing a further argument)

versō (1), to turn*

versor, versārī, versātus sum, to be occupied in, be involved in* C13

versūra, -ae, *f.,* exchanging one creditor for another, borrowing, application for a loan

versus, -ūs, *m.,* line of writing, line of verse* A8

vērus, -a, -um, *adj.,* true*

vester, vestra, vestrum, *adj.,* yours (pl.), your*

vestīmentum, -ī, *n.,* garment, (pl.) clothes*

vestiō, -īre, -īvī, -ītum, to dress

vestis, -is, *f.,* clothes, attire* C2

vetus, veteris, *adj.,* old* C5

vetustās, -ātis, *f.,* old age

vetustus, -a, -um, *adj.,* old*

vexō (1), to trouble, harass

via, -ae, *f.,* road*

victor, -ōris, *m.,* victor* C4

videō, -ēre, vīdī, vīsum, to see, (passive) seem*

vīlla, -ae, *f.,* country house, villa*

vincō, -ere, vīcī, victum, to conquer, defeat*

vinculum, -ī, *n.,* chain, fetter*

vīnum, -ī, *n.,* wine* C5

violenter, *adv.,* violently

violō (1), to violate, harm

vir, virī, *m.,* man*

virga, -ae, *f.,* twig, stick* C13

virgō, -inis, *f.,* virgin, girl of marriageable age* A9

virtūs, -ūtis, *f.,* virtue, courage* C5

vīs, —, *f. pl.,* **vīrēs, vīrium,** force, strength; **prō vīribus,** with all one's might*

vīta, -ae, *f.,* life*

vitium, -ī, *n.,* vice* C5

vītō (1), to avoid

vīvō, -ere, vīxī, vīctum, to live*

vīvus, -a, -um, *adj.,* alive

vix, *adv.,* hardly* C7

vocō (1), to call*

volō, velle, voluī, —, to want* C7

volūmen, -ūminis, *n.,* book, volume* A8

voluntās, -tātis, *f.,* will* C13

volvō, -ere, volvī, volūtum, to turn round* C14

vōs, *personal pronoun,* you (pl.)*

vōx, vōcis, *f.,* voice* C2

vulgus, -ī, *n.,* common people, general public* A7

vulnerō (1), to wound*

vulnus, -eris, *n.,* wound*

vultus, -ūs, *m.,* face* C2

ILLUSTRATION CREDITS

CHAPTER 1

Shamrocks (© 2009 Shutterstock Images LLC)

St. Patrick Statue (© 2009 Shutterstock Images LLC)

Bede Woodcut (© 2009 Jupiter Images Corp.)

CHAPTER 2

Hoher Markt, Vienna Clock (© 2009 Shutterstock Images LLC)

Charlemagne as Roman Emperor (© 2009 Jupiter Images Corp.)

Charlemagne Portrait (© 2009 Jupiter Images Corp.)

CHAPTER 3

Statue of Cicero, Palace of Justice, Rome (© 2009 Shutterstock Images LLC)

Hildegard von Bingen (© Creative Commons 1.0)

Astrolabe Engraving (© 2009 Shutterstock Images LLC)

CHAPTER 4

Statue of Godfrey, Brussels, Belgium (© 2009 Shutterstock Images LLC)

German Crusader Knight (© 2009 Jupiter Images Corp.)

CHAPTER 5

Medieval Wineshop Sign (© 2009 Shutterstock Images LLC)

Medieval Goblet (© 2009 Shutterstock Images LLC)

CHAPTER 6

Sir Henry Irving, Shakespearean Actor (© 2009 Jupiter Images Corp.)

CHAPTER 7

Roman Forum (© 2009 Shutterstock Images LLC)

Neoclassical Bust of Julius Caesar (© 2009 Shutterstock Images LLC)

CHAPTER 8

Engraving of Livy and Sallust (© 2009 Jupiter Images Corp.)

CHAPTER 9

Neptune Fountain, Gdańsk, Poland (© 2009 Shutterstock Images LLC)

Aeolus (© 2009 Shutterstock Images LLC)

Dürer's Engraving of Erasmus (© 2009 Jupiter Images Corp.)

CHAPTER 10

Holbein's Erasmus (© 2009 Jupiter Images Corp.)

CHAPTER 11

Woodcut from More's Utopia (© 2009 Jupiter Images Corp.)

Anne Boleyn (© 2009 Jupiter Images Corp.)

Catherine Parr (© 2009 Jupiter Images Corp.)

CHAPTER 12

Ferdinand Engraving (© 2009 Jupiter Images Corp.)

Columbus's Voyage (© 2009 Jupiter Images Corp.)

CHAPTER 13

Columbus Lands (© 2009 Jupiter Images Corp.)

Columbus with Spyglass (© 2009 Jupiter Images Corp.)

CHAPTER 14

Galileo Presents to the Muses (© 2009 Jupiter Images Corp.)

Copernicus (© 2009 Shutterstock Images LLC)

Kepler's Star Polyhedras (© 2009 Jupiter Images Corp.)

Anna Maria van Schurman (Public Domain)

CHAPTER 15

Man Rappeling (© 2009 Shutterstock Images LLC)

Trees (© 2009 Shutterstock Images LLC)